APPROACHES TO THE SHORT STORY

Approaches to the
SHORT STORY

Collected and Edited by

NEIL D. ISAACS

THE CITY COLLEGE, NEW YORK

and

LOUIS H. LEITER

UNIVERSITY OF NEBRASKA

Chandler Publishing Company

SAN FRANCISCO

COPYRIGHT © 1963 BY CHANDLER PUBLISHING COMPANY

LIBRARY OF CONGRESS CATALOG CARD NO. 63-9887

DESIGNED BY JAMES MENNICK

PRINTED IN THE UNITED STATES OF AMERICA

"The Open Parable: Demonstration and Definition" by Richard M. Eastman is from *College English* (October 1960) pp. 15-18. Copyright, 1960, by the National Council of Teachers of English. Reprinted with the permission of the National Council of Teachers of English and Richard M. Eastman. ◼ "The Double View: Melville's 'The Lightning-Rod Man'" by Harry B. Wilson is an original essay written especially for the present collection. ◼ "Sleepy Oppositions" by Irving Malin is an original essay written especially for the present collection. ◼ "Sire de Malétroit's Door" by Eric LaGuardia first appeared in *American Imago* and is reprinted here by permission of that publication. ◼ "A Worn Path" by Eudora Welty is from *A Curtain of Green and Other Stories*. Copyright, 1941, by Eudora Welty. Reprinted from *A Curtain of Green* by Eudora Welty by permission of Harcourt, Brace & World, Inc. ◼ "Life for Phoenix" by Neil D. Isaacs first appeared in the *Sewanee Review* (Winter 1962/63) and is reprinted here by permission of that publication. ◼ "Blake's Urizen as Hawthorne's Ethan Brand" by Glenn Pedersen is copyright © 1958, by The Regents of the University of California. Reprinted by permission of The Regents. ◼ "The Secret Sharer" by Joseph Conrad is reprinted by permission of J. M. Dent & Sons Ltd., Publishers. ◼ "Echo Structures: Conrad's *The Secret Sharer*" by Louis H. Leiter is reprinted from *Twentieth Century Literature*, Vol. 5, No. 4 (January 1960), pp. 159-175. ◼ "Stephen Crane's 'The Bride Comes to Yellow Sky'" by George Monteiro is an original essay written especially for the present collection.

To the Memory of

ROBERT GALE NOYES

TEACHER, FRIEND, GENTLE MAN

FOREWORD

Approaches to the Short Story proceeds from a number of premises: that literature can be studied; that, if it can be studied, it should be treated as a subject for study; that the methods of that study may be formulated systematically; that the system so arrived at—criticism—is necessary and important; that literature is an art form; that the short story, a type of literature, can be studied through the methods of criticism.

Approaches to the Short Story is not intended to formulate a system. It is not at all a closed book; it is an open one, intended to point toward the wealth of the short story as an art form and toward the wealth of critical approaches available to students of the form. The stories treated have been included, not only so that the theses of the essays may be demonstrated, but also that the reader may see what *more* can be done with them, perhaps by applying the methods of the *other* essays.

The introductory essay (by Richard M. Eastman, beginning with his own original story) suggests what we are all about. For in a sense every story is an "open parable," exposed for the master (teacher, critic, student) to explicate, to illuminate both story and audience (and sometimes author as well).

In the next essay (by Harry B. Wilson), the importance of interpretation, of finding the content, is emphasized: "This is the point of parable and allegory and fable: interpretation is not gratuitous; it is necessary; it is what *finds* the content."

The two essays that follow (Irving Malin on "The Legend of Sleepy Hollow" and Eric LaGuardia on "The Sire de Malétroit's Door") reflect a Freudian orientation, the first implicitly but pervasively, the second explicitly in thorough detail. This does not suggest the editors' bias; it suggests, rather, how integral a part of our reading apparatus the psychology has become.

The fifth essay (Neil D. Isaacs on "A Worn Path") is an exercise in the elementary analysis of the imagery and allusions of a short story. It is the shortest piece; many of the statements are left for the reader to test against the story and work out in his own reading.

The following essay (Glenn Pedersen on "Ethan Brand") shows the value of comparing one work of art with another. This approach, held in disrepute these days, is demonstrably effective here, elucidating the workings of the particular story and also making a point about the criticism of art in general.

Next, Conrad's "The Secret Sharer" is treated in an essay (by Louis H. Leiter) which also begins with analysis of imagery. In rich detail it proceeds to an original statement of the structure and form of the story.

The critical method used in the last essay (by George Monteiro) stresses "the esthetic and thematic function of reflexive diction, image clusters, the double-self (or 'split-image'), and an Apollonian-Dionysian pattern" and makes explicit Crane's themes by analyzing, in Crane's story, the use of these devices and concepts.

None of the pieces is meant as a definitive study of its story. If anything, they are all deliberately contentious, or at least tendentious, an epithet applied by R. P. Blackmur, with tempered opprobrium, to much provocative criticism.

Following each essay except the first two are comments that suggest possibilities for further application of approaches. These comments are designed—with the entire book—to promote broader and deeper critical reading. The first essay provides its own comments, and the questions following the second essay provide examples of the kinds of challenges the reader can with profit put to himself regarding all the stories in this collection.

NDI

LHL

October, 1962

CONTENTS

APPROACHES TO THE SHORT STORY

The Open Parable:
Demonstration and Definition

RICHARD M. EASTMAN

I

Signs of rust were everywhere. The deck, instead of showing the trim vacuity of an efficient merchant ship, was befouled with rope ends, grease patches, bits of splintered box. It listed perpetually, at an angle to make one stumble if he went by first appearances.

When a bell quavered out in the cold salt-laden fog, I noticed a general drifting below decks. I followed to the mess and there was fed without challenge, in fact I seemed to be taken for a member of the crew. It came to me that if some of the crew had seen long service on this ship, others had boarded more recently. They had a way of taking each other as strangers in a world of strangers, and talked with a kind of time-filling intimacy.

Although I had intended at the earliest chance to find the captain and demand an explanation of my being here, after mess I was caught up again, in the drift above deck. There I found myself rather expected to join in the splicing of old rope bits. It seemed to me then that I might as well. All I could gather in that first afternoon on that gray sea was that these men existed without pride in their work, without the foretaste of pleasures in any port. Quietly they despised their ship and respectfully they detested her captain—why, I could not determine, except that they had surely expected more of him than this long pitching through dreary seas in a rusted hulk.

Just before dusk settled that dark day, I did meet one of the ship's officers, the second mate. He alone on that ship impressed me with vigor and youth. He recognized me as a newcomer; rather, he greeted me in that freshness by which the trusting spirit makes out all the world a new place.

"You've joined a great ship," he said. "True, she needs repair. Is there anything really alive which doesn't? She's small and powerful, thoroughly navigable, and we're in the most propitious seas for commerce, and above all we've the crew. Without a first-rate crew," he told me, "you can do nothing." His voice thinned into a higher pitch. "What's important is that our hearts should beat by a single determined pulse. With that I've no doubt we shall drive our way out of this fog bank; we shall take our place as one of the finest carriers of the ocean."

You cannot help thawing to such men, and I found that the other crew members for all their discontent liked the second mate as well as I did. As for just why I was on the ship and what I was to do, he could not say, but he told me the captain knew everything and he would personally speak to the captain about my case. With that I had to rest. The next day and the next week I heard no more from the second mate. Occasionally I did see on the ship's bridge a dignified heavy figure which I was told was that of the captain, but I never heard him speak. Only, from time to time, we saw the second mate standing next, listening respectfully and then coming down to organize, if I may use that word, the heartless activities on deck.

So I report these first days simply because they were the first. The many others were alike, except that the ship seemed to list more and more. Once on passing through the hold, I heard the slosh of water, and I was frightened to think how deep the ship was actually riding. But the others shrugged. They had been through the same shock. Through some miracle of mediocrity the ship floated on. As for the engine-shafts, they ground so badly that the bulkheads trembled. Or a shaft would snarl, die, then resume twisting in irresolute agony. The second mate assured us that the engineers had received advice from the captain which would keep the screws turning. I learned before long that the sense of purpose we did have came entirely from these second-hand reports of the second mate, who always behaved as if every shudder of the ship had been planned by the captain.

What sank day by day, even more than the ship, was the morale of the crew. Men can stand hard treatment. They can stand privation, rise to dangers. What we had to stand was the staunch silhouetted dummy of the captain's figure seen in the fog swirls on the bridge—the picture perhaps of dignity but also of an inaccessible will, so reserved to itself as to cast a mere comfortless shadow upon our own lives. The ship itself served no apparent land purposes. Even the oldest crew members could not swear that the cargo was cargo or perhaps only ballast. In their mounting bitterness these men talked mutiny more than once, only to fall silent before the radiant dismay of the second mate.

How long was I on that ship? A good part of my life I should say. After a long while we noticed that the captain was absent from the bridge. Sick, said the second mate, or perusing the charts, but still in command. I liked that second mate. On a really good ship he would have made a fine executive, indispensable to his chief and loved by his crews. As it was, he began to exhaust us by his repeated drafts upon our reserves of good will. We had once been fired with his imagination; on that account we now saw all the more bleakly that the ship had nearly merged into the gray oblivion of that boundless ocean.

So on a winter day the water washed below decks in knee-deep torrents. The seas were pouring over the bulwarks as I found the older crewmen breaking out the boats. The second mate stood near the davits, clutching at us to stick by the captain; the ship could not go on without her great crew. I thought we would need to use violence against that second mate, but when the moment came for the tackles to creak and the lifeboats to drop, he stood aside. The men scurried into the boats and called over for him to follow.

"There's no hope," they called. "You're wasting yourself. If necessary, bring the captain, we'll wait that long."

"No," he said. "As a matter of fact, the captain may be dead, but this ship is still seaworthy, and if I must I will go on alone until I can get another crew together. A man lives only once, after all. This was my chance."

These last words he said to me. With a regretful shake of his hand I followed the others into the lifeboat and we cast away. We rose and fell over the blindly tumultuous waves and watched the hulk of that small gray dilapidated ship as it pounded painfully toward an ever-receding horizon. It did not sink while we watched it, nor although we got back to land did I ever hear of its wreckage being found. Sometimes I wonder if that rotten old piece of iron is still sliding through the seas with that strange second mate trying to act as its heart and soul.

II

The parable-story as its comes to us through the Hebrew and Greek traditions is enclosed in a single frame of application which makes it easily accessible. Jesus' story of the Good Samaritan, for example, is prefaced with an abstract question: "Who is my neighbor?" The story plainly presents a test situation (the wounded victim in the road) and three possible reactions (that of the priest, the Levite, and the Samaritan). The preferred listener-response of admiration for the Samaritan is unmistakable. The story closes with a reference to the topic ("Which was neighbor?") and an answer ("He that showed mercy" . . . "Go and do thou likewise"). Any difficulty must be invented by asking the story to be what it is not; that is, an analytical ethical discourse which distinguishes and categorizes the circumstances under which one may know that he is in the Good Samaritan position. As itself—a parable, a brief and plausible allegory, a concrete analogue of a general ethical situation—Jesus' story stands single and unblurred, a "closed" image.

When consistently expanded to include some complexity of incident, distinctness of characterization, and fullness of setting, the closed parable becomes a story with its own narrative appeals. A list of examples would include Dickens' *A Christmas Carol,* George Eliot's *Silas Marner,* Hawthorne's "The Minister's Black Veil," Tolstoy's "God Sees the Truth But Waits," E. M. Forester's "The Other Side of the Hedge," and William Sansom's "The Long Sheet." In all, however, the ethical analogy which is the animating idea of the parable remains clearly distinguishable beneath a consistent narrative surface.

III

In the foregoing tale of "The Phantom Ship," however, the narrative surface is ruptured. The fictional world fails to keep true to itself. How did the narrator get aboard? The ship has evidently been floundering in the fog-bank indefinitely; yet the narrator's arrival is taken for granted. Why is there no first mate? If the ship is so tangible as to show rust, rope ends, and grinding engine-shafts, how is it that no activity of crew or captain seems efficient for keeping the ship in motion? Such instability of detail hinders the reader in making out a simple analogic structure to the story. He may well begin to drift as in a dream, straining to see the latent shapes behind the distorted manifest content of the tale.

He is in short reading an "open parable": a small genre of modern narrative brought to high intensity by such writers as Kafka and Beckett. Its difficulties rise from the misapplication of conventional reading attitudes, usually abetted by the logical refusal of its authors to explain "intention." Hence the present demonstration, arranged in the workshop so to speak, may serve an instructive purpose.

If "The Phantom Ship" discourages quick orientation of the reader—and this is the first characteristic of its method—it none the less employs a central situation of high metaphoric power. The ship at sea has suggested hundreds of correspondences to human life. Furthermore, the present story adds the folklore motif of the ghost ship, heavy in mystery, fearfulness, and despair. Through such devices the author of the open parable charges his material so that the reader, deliberately troubled, will begin to infer a series of possible correspondences. The phantom ship may suggest a nation or an institution foundering in mismanagement, with only a gleam of its once-bright purpose, in the person of the second mate, to prevent the total eclipse of morale. Or the ship may figure a moribund religion, with the captain as dying god and the second mate as a desperately confident priesthood. Certain existentialists might see the ship as human life—without definite origin or guaranteed destiny, without any of the significance traditionally assigned to it.

Only the one himself who lives, the second mate, can give it meaning, and even then, ultimately, only on his own authority (hence the vanishing of the captain).

Like a kind of literary Rorschach blot, the open parable apparently puts it up to the reader to perform the creative act, to take his own direction so that he may find, in the general richness of theme, an ethical pattern which speaks most directly to him. This is the first pleasure of the genre. But the open parable is a controlled and controlling art-work, not a random blot. The persistent reader—and the very form of the story invites him to persist—will find that "The Phantom Ship" yields not a mere plurality of expressions, but a system of them having as matrix the basic question of *commitment to imperfect enterprises*. Such a master-pattern gives the open parable its unity. Moreover, the attentive reader will discover that no one expression will prove out as *the* meaning. Not only does "The Phantom Ship" omit to specify whether its application is political or religious or existential, but it is so constructed with certain opaque, irreducible details as to block the final verification of any one hypothesis. Thus if the "phantom ship" is human life and the second mate is the "one who lives," what can one confidently make of the narrator? Or the crew which abandons ship?

The emotional response sought by the parable may similarly be kept open. By its balancing of sympathetic and antipathetic detail, the reader is hindered from endorsing any one character or any one theme. Should one admire the second mate, or pity him? Is the narrator a faithless rat who "scurries" from the ship, or a compassionate observer, slow to leave the doomed man whose hand he graps on the flooding deck? Indeed, in "The Phantom Ship" this ambivalence is thematically important in underscoring such questions as these: Is "commitment to an imperfect enterprise," after all, heroic or pathetic or simply inevitable? Can one really know until he comes to such a commitment himself?

Through a designed instability, therefore, the open parable can present a single ethical motif with variations of indefinite number and strength. The experienced reader will accordingly refrain from any quick allegorical interpretation. Rather he will enjoy the widening shock of reference. This I think is why the author of an open parable usually declines to explain his work, and why his explanation, if granted, is sometimes felt to be impertinent: any explicit limiting of reference simply defeats the artistic end of the form itself.

The reader who wishes to prove the attractions of the open parable to a richer degree must certainly come to the fiction of Franz Kafka: especially *The Trial*, "The Penal Colony," "The Hunger Artist," and "Metamorphosis." He will find a severer challenge in Samuel Beckett, whose novel *Molloy* and play *Endgame* are especially fine examples. Other specimens of the literature include James Gould Cozzens's novelette *Castaway*, Shirley Jackson's short story "The Lottery," Friedrich Duerrenmatt's play *The Visit*, and such plays of Eugéne Ionesco as *The Chairs, The Lesson*, and *The New Tenant*. Robert Browning's "Childe Roland to the Dark Tower Came" furnishes an early example of the genre; and it would be quite possible to find open-parable features in Melville's *Moby-Dick*.

In detailing the peculiar magic of the open parable I do not mean to oversell it. Any reader condemned to read its literature for month after month would find its dream-tone monotonous, its characters flat, its themes too coyly elusive. In the world-wide commerce of literature, the open parable is itself a "phantom ship"—not fitted to carry heavy cargoes but specially able in its ghostly outlines to evoke the philosophical excitement which transforms all reading into an exploration of the human spirit.

I

The Lightning-Rod Man

HERMAN MELVILLE

What grand irregular thunder, thought I, standing on my hearth-stone among the Acroceraunian hills, as the scattered bolts boomed overhead, and crashed down among the valleys, every bolt followed by zigzag irradiations, and swift slants of sharp rain, which audibly rang, like a charge of spear-points, on my low shingled roof. I suppose, though, that the mountains hereabouts break and churn up the thunder, so that it is far more glorious here than on the plain. Hark!—someone at the door. Who is this that chooses a time of thunder for making calls? And why don't he, man-fashion, use the knocker, instead of making that doleful undertaker's clatter with his fist against the hollow panel? But let him in. Ah, here he comes. "Good day, sir": an entire stranger. "Pray be seated." What is that strange-looking walking-stick he carries? "A fine thunderstorm, sir."

"Fine?—Awful!"

"You are wet. Stand here on the hearth before the fire."

"Not for worlds!"

The stranger still stood in the exact middle of the cottage, where he had first planted himself. His singularity impelled a closer scrutiny. A lean, gloomy figure. Hair dark and lank, mattedly streaked over his brow. His sunken pitfalls of eyes were ringed by indigo halos, and played with an innocuous sort of lightning: the gleam without the bolt. The whole man was dripping. He stood in a puddle on the bare oak floor: his strange walking-stick vertically resting at his side.

It was a polished copper rod, four feet long, lengthwise attached to a neat wooden staff by insertion into two balls of greenish glass, ringed with copper bands. The metal rod terminated at the top tripodwise, in three keen tines, brightly gilt. He held the thing by the wooden part alone.

"Sir," said I, bowing politely, "have I the honour of a visit from that illustrious god, Jupiter Tonans? So stood he in the Greek statue of old, grasping the lightning-bolt. If you be he, or his viceroy, I have to thank you for this noble storm you have brewed among our mountains. Listen: That was a glorious peal. Ah, to a lover of the majestic, it is a good thing to have the Thunderer himself in one's cottage. The thunder grows finer for that. But pray be seated. This old rush-bottomed armchair, I grant, is a poor substitute for your evergreen throne on Olympus; but condescend to be seated."

While I thus pleasantly spoke, the stranger eyed me, half in wonder, and half in a strange sort of horror; but did not move a foot.

"Do, sir, be seated; you need to be dried ere going forth again."

I planted the chair invitingly on the broad hearth, where a little fire had been kindled that afternoon to dissipate the dampness, not the cold; for it was early in the month of September.

But without heeding my solication, and still standing in the middle of the floor, the stranger gazed at me portentously and spoke.

"Sir," said he, "excuse me; but instead of my accepting your invitation to be seated on the hearth there, I solemnly warn *you,* that you had best accept *mine,* and stand with me in the middle of the room. Good heavens!" he cried, starting—"there is another of those awful crashes. I warn you, sir, quit the hearth."

"Mr. Jupiter Tonans," said I, quietly rolling my body on the stone, "I stand very well here."

"Are you so horridly ignorant, then," he cried, "as not to know, that by far the most dangerous part of a house, during such a terrific tempest as this, is the fireplace?"

"Nay, I did not know that," involuntarily stepping upon the first board next to the stone.

The stranger now assumed such an unpleasant air of successful admonition, that—quite involuntarily again—I stepped back
upon the hearth, and threw myself into the erectest, proudest
posture I could command. But I said nothing.

"For heaven's sake," he cried, with a strange mixture of alarm
and intimidation—"for heaven's sake, get off the hearth! Know
you not, that the heated air and soot are conductors;—to say
nothing of those immense fire-dogs? Quit the spot—I conjure—I
command you."

"Mr. Jupiter Tonans, I am not accustomed to be commanded
in my own house."

"Call me not by that pagan name. You are profane in this
time of terror."

"Sir, will you be so good as to tell me your business? If you
seek shelter from the storm, you are welcome, so long as you be
civil; but if you come on business, open it forthwith. Who are
you?"

"I am a dealer in lightning-rods," said the stranger, softening
his tone; "my special business is——Merciful heaven! what a
crash!—Have you ever been struck—your premises, I mean? No?
It's best to be provided";—significantly rattling his metallic staff
on the floor;—"by nature, there are no castles in thunder-storms;
yet, say but the word, and of this cottage I can make a Gibraltar
by a few waves of this wand. Hark, what Himalayas of concus-
sions!"

"You interrupted yourself; your special business you were
about to speak of."

"My special business is to travel the country for orders for
lightning-rods. This is my specimen rod," tapping his staff; "I
have the best of references"—fumbling in his pockets. "In Criggan last month, I put up three-and-twenty rods on only five
buildings."

"Let me see. Was it not at Criggan last week, about midnight on Saturday, that the steeple, the big elm, and the as-
sembly-room cupola were struck? Any of your rods there?"

"Not on the tree and cupola, but the steeple."

"Of what use is your rod, then?"

"Of life-and-death use. But my workman was heedless. In fitting the rod at top to the steeple, he allowed a part of the metal to graze the tin sheeting. Hence the accident. Not my fault, but his. Hark!"

"Never mind. That clap burst quite loud enough to be heard without finger-pointing. Did you hear of the event at Montreal last year? A servant girl struck at her bedside with a rosary in her hand; the beads being metal. Does your beat extend into the Canadas?"

"No. And I hear that there, iron rods only are in use. They should have *mine,* which are copper. Iron is easily fused. Then they draw out the rod so slender, that it has not body enough to conduct the full electric current. The metal melts; the building is destroyed. My copper rods never act so. Those Canadians are fools. Some of them knob the rod at the top, which risks a deadly explosion, instead of imperceptibly carrying down the current into the earth, as this sort of rod does. *Mine* is the only true rod. Look at it. Only one dollar a foot."

"This abuse of your own calling in another might make one distrustful with respect to yourself."

"Hark! The thunder becomes less muttering. It is nearing us, and nearing the earth, too. Hark! One crammed crash! All the vibrations made one by nearness. Another flash. Hold!"

"What do you?" I said, seeing him now, instantaneously relinquishing his staff, lean intently forward toward the window, with his right fore and middle fingers on his left wrist.

But ere the words had well escaped me, another exclamation escaped him.

"Crash! only three pulses—less than a third of a mile off— yonder, somewhere in that wood. I passed three stricken oaks there, ripped out new and glittering. The oak draws lightning more than other timber, having iron in solution in its sap. Your floor here seems oak."

"Heart-of-oak. From the peculiar time of your call upon me, I suppose you purposely select stormy weather for your journeys. When the thunder is roaring, you deem it an hour peculiarly favourable for producing impressions favourable to your trade."

"Hark!—Awful!"

"For one who would arm others with fearlessness, you seem unbeseemingly timorous yourself. Common men choose fair weather for their travels; you choose thunder-storms; and yet——"

"That I travel in thunder-storms, I grant; but not without particular precautions, such as only a lightning-rod man may know. Hark! Quick—look at my specimen rod. Only one dollar a foot."

"A very fine rod, I dare say. But what are these particular precautions of yours? Yet first let me close yonder shutters; the slanting rain is beating through the sash. I will bar up."

"Are you mad? Know you not that yon iron bar is a swift conductor? Desist."

"I will simply close the shutters, then, and call my boy to bring me a wooden bar. Pray, touch the bell-pull there."

"Are you frantic? That bell-wire might blast you. Never touch bell-wire in a thunder-storm, nor ring a bell of any sort."

"Nor those in belfries? Pray, will you tell me where and how one may be safe in a time like this? Is there any part of my house I may touch with hopes of my life?"

"There is; but not where you now stand. Come away from the wall. The current will sometimes run down a wall, and—a man being a better conductor than a wall—it would leave the wall and run into him. Swoop! *That* must have fallen very nigh. That must have been globular lightning."

"Very probably. Tell me at once, which is, in your opinion, the safest part of this house?"

"This room, and this one spot in it where I stand. Come hither."

"The reasons first."

"Hark!—after the flash the gust—the sashes shiver—the house, the house!—Come hither to me!"

"The reasons, if you pease."

"Come hither to me!"

"Thank you again, I think I will try my old stand—the hearth. And now, Mr. Lightning-rod man, in the pauses of the thunder, be so good as to tell me your reasons for esteeming this one room of the house the safest, and your own one standpoint there the safest spot in it."

There was now a little cessation of the storm for a while. The Lightning-rod man seemed relieved, and replied:

"Your house is a one-storied house, with an attic and a cellar; this room is between. Hence its comparative safety. Because lightning sometimes passes from the clouds to the earth, and sometimes from the earth to the clouds. Do you comprehend?— and I choose the middle of the room, because, if the lightning should strike the house at all, it would come down the chimney or walls; so, obviously, the further you are from them, the better. Come hither to me, now."

"Presently. Something you just said, instead of alarming me, has strangely inspired confidence."

"What have I said?"

"You said that sometimes lightning flashes from the earth to the clouds."

"Ay, the returning-stroke, as it is called; when the earth, being overcharged with the fluid, flashes its surplus upward."

"The returning-stroke; that is, from earth to sky. Better and better. But come hear on the hearth and dry yourself."

"I am better here, and better wet."

"How?"

"It is the safest thing you can do—Hark, again!—to get yourself thoroughly drenched in a thunder-storm. Wet clothes are better conductors than the body; and so, if the lightning strike, it might pass down the wet clothes without touching the body. The storm deepens again. Have you a rug in the house? Rugs are non-conductors. Get one, that I may stand on it here, and you, too. The skies blacken—it is dusk at noon. Hark!—the rug, the rug!"

I gave him one; while the hooded mountains seemed closing and tumbling into the cottage.

"And now, since our being dumb will not help us," said I, resuming my place, "let me hear your precautions in travelling during the thunder-storms."

"Wait till this one is past."

"Nay, proceed with the precautions. You stand in the safest possible place according to your own account. Go on."

"Briefly, then. I avoid pine-trees, high houses, lonely barns, upland pastures, running water, flocks of cattle and sheep, a crowd of men. If I travel on foot—as to-day—I do not walk fast; if in my buggy, I touch not its back or sides; if on horseback, I dismount and lead the horse. But of all things, I avoid tall men."

"Do I dream? Man avoid man? and in danger-time, too."

"Tall men in a thunder-storm I avoid. Are you so grossly ignorant as not to know, that the height of a six-footer is sufficient to discharge an electric cloud upon him? Are not lonely Kentuckians, ploughing, smit in the unfinished furrow? Nay, if the six-footer stand by running water, the cloud will sometimes *select* him as its conductor to that running water. Hark! Sure, yon black pinnacle is split. Yes, a man is a good conductor. The lightning goes through and through a man, but only peels a tree. But, sir, you have kept me so long answering your questions that I have not yet come to business. Will you order one of my rods? Look at this specimen one. See: it is of the best of copper. Copper's the best conductor. Your house is low; but being upon the mountains, that lowness does not one whit depress it. You mountaineers are most exposed. In mountainous countries the lightning-rod man should have most business. Look at the specimen, sir. One rod will answer for a house so small as this. Look over these recommendations. One rod, sir; cost, only twenty dollars. Hark! There go all the granite Taconics and Hoosics dashed together like pebbles. By the sound, that must have struck something. An elevation of five feet about the house will protect twenty feet radius all about the rod. Only twenty dollars, sir—a dollar a foot. Hark!—Dreadful!—Will you order? Will you buy? Shall I put down your name? Think of being a heap of charred offal, like a haltered horse burnt in his stall; and all in one flash!"

"You pretended envoy extraordinary and minister plenipotentiary to and from Jupiter Tonans," laughed I; "you mere man who come here to put you and your pipe-stem between clay and sky, do you think that because you can strike a bit of green light from the Leyden jar, that you can thoroughly avert the supernal bolt? Your rod rusts, or breaks, and where are you?

Who has empowered you, you Tetzel,* to peddle round your indulgences from divine ordinations? The hairs of our heads are numbered, and the days of our lives. In thunder as in sunshine, I stand at ease in the hands of my God. False negotiator, away! See, the scroll of the storm is rolled back; the house is unharmed; and in the blue heavens I read in the rainbow, that the Deity will not, of purpose, make war on man's earth."

"Impious wretch!" foamed the stranger, blackening in the face as the rainbow beamed, "I will publish your infidel notions."

The scowl grew blacker on his face; the indigo circles enlarged round his eyes as the storm-rings round the midnight moon. He sprang upon me; his tri-forked thing at my heart.

I seized it; I snapped it; I dashed it; I trod it; and dragging the dark lightning-king out of my door, flung his elbowed, copper sceptre after him.

But spite of my treatment, and spite of my dissuasive talk of him to my neighbours, the Lightning-rod man still dwells in the land; still travels in storm-time, and drives a brave trade with the fears of man.

* *Editors' note:* The immediate cause of Luther's break with the Church was Tetzel's sale of indulgences.

The Double View: Melville's "The Lightning-Rod Man"

HARRY B. WILSON

It would be hard to find a simpler action than the one which serves Melville in "The Lightning-Rod Man." It is hardly more than an encounter, so bare that "plot" would be a pretentious term for it. Two men talk for a short while; one of them is ejected from the house; there is a brief summarized glimpse of the future; and no more. Nor is this "action" accompanied by a full characterization—in the sense of giving the minutiae of individual tastes, gestures, tones of voice—or a depiction of physical reality. Detailed reality is as bare as the action itself: a house in a mountainous region during an electrical storm; of the room where the men stand and talk we know little more than that it contains an old rush-bottomed armchair and a fireplace with a fire burning in it.

Because the story seems to hover outside or above reality, it asks to be called something other than a story. A fable perhaps or a parable—yet even the illustrative struggle which "proves" the moral in, say, La Fontaine, is missing in the Melville piece. Nothing is proved here (certainly the narrator's safety at the end of the story does not "prove" that man is exempt from lightning bolts); merely, two attitudes or angles of vision are presented. If one must find another genre, the one-act play or the dramatic monologue would be the best choices. But the label provided by a genre does little except identify. The identification is valuable to the extent that it denotes characteristics of form which prepare the reader. But it does not go beyond this: and beyond this is where the individuality of a story or

16

poem or parable begins to manifest itself; where art begins to deepen in the form of technique, along with meaning. So the question "What?" needs to elicit more than a label; it needs to call up the connotative substance, the drift of metaphor, symbol, myth, allusion that give weight and "meaning" to such a work as "The Lightning-Rod Man."

"Give" is perhaps misleading; for it suggests that whatever is supplied by symbol and myth is a kind of extra which the reader can have if he is so inclined, but there is no need, since he has the reality of the action to begin with. But Melville's story on the level of sheer reality (or discursive detail and action, the drift of detail in such a story as Eudora Welty's "A Worn Path" or Conrad's "The Secret Sharer") is hardly more than a skeletal joke about a salesman who doesn't make a sale. It is only when one goes beyond—or *behind*—the discursive action that one finds anything of any consequence. This is the point of parable and allegory and fable: interpretation is not gratuitous; it is necessary; it is what *finds* the content.

In getting behind the action of "The Lightning-Rod Man" the first thing to note is that the narrator is intensely preoccupied with the storm that is going on outside his house. He registers the display of light and noise; relates it to his "low-shingled roof"; and goes on to explain to himself *why* the thunder is so loud in this part of the country. When somebody knocks at his door he wonders who it is "that chooses a time of thunder for making calls." In the exchange of talk and the action that follows, the concern is for lightning—its nature, behavior, dangers. The narrator and the stranger speak of nothing else. One may say that the outside world dominates the inside, or that the two characters are immersed in what is occurring outside the house. Nor is this all. For the stranger, besides making, upon the door, a sound which is like the thunders, is a kind of embodiment of the storm itself: "A lean, gloomy figure. Hair dark and lank, mattedly streaked over his brow. His sunken pitfalls of eyes were ringed by indigo halos, and played with an innocuous sort of lightning: the gleam without the bolt. The whole man was dripping." The stranger's very humanness seems to be doubtful, for when the narrator hears the clatter of the man's fist at the door, he asks: "And why don't he, man-fashion, use the knocker . . . ?" (This trait is demonstrated again at the end of the story when the stranger reveals his isolation, during storms, from people in groups, and from tall men.) After scrutinizing his visitor the narrator pretends—or assumes, we aren't clearly told—that he is a god, Jupiter, in his form of bearer of the thunderbolt; or else is Jupiter's viceroy. He credits him with the storm, and carries on the comparison with the god until the stranger, annoyed, asks him to stop. The fact that this is all done in jest does not weaken the point: the narrator's concentration upon the storm.

This preoccupation with the storm, and the appearance of an "other worldly" stranger connected with it (he embodies it and sells protection against it) , may serve as evidence for regarding the stranger *not* as a real man but as a creation—a projection—of the narrator's. The reason for the act of projection could be fear of the storm's power. Thus it is clear why the stranger chooses a "time of thunder" for making calls. This is the time when the narrator's fears occur. What follows is then a kind of game, or struggle, in which the narrator faces his fears, and finally defeats or exorcises them.

At first glance the evidence would seem to be against seeing the narrator's response to the storm as one of fear. He praises the thunder as "grand" and "glorious" and the whole storm as "noble." And throughout the conversation he refuses to take the precautions urged upon him by the stranger: he will not come to the center of the room, the point of safety. Yet the very fact that he *does* praise the storm may be a sign of fear. Add to this his knowledgeability about recent catastrophes produced by lightning. Also, when the stranger first tells him that a hearth is the most dangerous part of a house during a storm, the narrator "involuntarily" steps off the stone. But when the stranger looks pleased, the narrator returns to the hearth—"involuntarily again"—and deliberately stands erect and proud there. From that moment on the narrator progressively rejects the stranger's urgings, and ends up breaking his rod (symbol, for the narrator, of his fear) and flinging him from the house: two acts which climax his act of subduing his fear. The stranger himself is, seemingly, as frightened of the storm as the narrator, seemingly, is not. He constantly warns the narrator of danger, sticks to the safest spot in the house, and begs for a rug. He is a veritable compendium of charms against lightning—both inside and outside a house. And he carries his precautionary measures to such lengths that he isolates himself during a storm; becomes a center of fearful *awareness,* his hopes fixed on his amulet, the lightning rod. In the last paragraph the narrator specifically connects the salesman with fear when he observes that "the Lightning-rod man still dwells in the land; still travels in storm-time, and drives a brave trade with the fears of man."

But to see the encounter between the two characters as a struggle in which the narrator clearly wins—that is, conquers his fears—is to risk a one-sided reading. For the narrator's exclamation, "See, the scroll of the storm is rolled back; the house is unharmed," can be taken as one of relief rather than one of triumph. Significantly it is at the end of the storm that he breaks the "copper sceptre" and drives the lightning-rod man out. Since the storm has ended, he no longer has any reason to be afraid, nor any need for the protection promised him by the lightning-rod man; he can dispense with both man and rod. He has "subdued" his fear only by no longer being face to face with what causes it. The ambiguity will become more noticeable if we remember that it is the *narrator* who draws from the stranger his precautions against lightning; the stranger does not volunteer them. Seen this way, the lightning-rod man is not only a projection of the narrator's fears; he is the use to which the narrator puts his fears, arriving, through them, at an assortment of precautions which will protect him.

Such an interpretation of the lightning-rod man—as the narrator's projection of his fears—is supported somewhat by the tone of the story: the immediate immersion in the *experiencing* of the storm, the switch from past to present tense (as if to signal that the events to be narrated are "outside" external time), and the locating of the events in the mountains (the narrator specifically observes that he is "above" the plains). This tone or drift may be Melville's way of signalling to the reader that what is to take place is not actual external occurrence but internal

and symbolic. Yet it must be admitted that for all the support
one can find, the lightning-rod man does not serve very well as
a projection of the narrator's fear. The reason he doesn't is that
the realistic detail, which would ordinarily produce, and in turn
be illuminated by, the *symbol* of the lightning-rod man as fear,
is so thin that the symbol has no active referent. There are not
enough contextual details to produce, explain, and justify it.
It is as if, in the ballad of "Barbery Allen," we were given the
thorn to symbolize Barbery's heartlessness but without any *preceding* evidence of her heartlessness to vitalize, and in turn be
vitalized by, the thorn. We are given the symbol alone for the
entire rich complex of which the symbol ought to be but a part.

An alternate interpretation, one which removes us from an
emotional to a philosophical plane, is this: to see the lightning-
rod man as the embodiment of some belief or attitude. We
note, first of all, the stance that the narrator takes in opposition to him. Their encounter is a conflict, but not so much of
personalities as of personified differences. On the surface this
comes out as the taking of precautions against lightning—keeping clear of dangerous spots and using the copper rod as insur-
ance against being struck—and the rejection of those precautions and the peddler of them. But these are only manifesta-
tions of a deeper difference: the relation between God and man,
nature and man.

To the lightning-rod dealer, God and nature are destructive
forces that must be negotiated with through ritual-like proscrip-
tions and stances. Though we see him at work only during a
particularly violent manifestation of natural destructiveness, we
can assume that his whole life is circumscribed by the precautions he reveals to the narrator: "I avoid pine-trees, high
houses, lonely barns, upland pastures, running water, flocks of
cattle and sheep, a crowd of men. . . . But of all things I avoid
tall men." His "special business" of taking orders for lightning
rods and the superstitions that attend it are symbolic of a way
of regarding God and nature, the everyday context of human
action, as capricious powers against whom protection must be
rigorously sought.

This view has, as superstition usually does, some of the marks of a system, one which suggests both science and religion—a religion noticeably mixed up with commerce (observe how often the dealer tries to *sell* his product—"Only one dollar a foot"—to the narrator). The lightning-rod man's utterances are delivered with all the assurance of scientific facts: "Those Canadians are fools. Some of them knob the rod at the top, which risks a deadly explosion, instead of imperceptibly carrying down the current into the earth, as [my] sort of rod does"; "The oak draws lightning more than other timber, having iron in solution in its sap"; "Your house is a one-storied house, with an attic and a cellar; this room is between. Hence its comparative safety. Because lightning sometimes passes from the clouds to the earth, and sometimes from the earth to the clouds . . . the earth, being overcharged with the fluid, flashes its surplus upward"; "Wet clothes are a better conductor than the body; . . . Rugs are non-conductors." Whether these *are* facts is not relevant; what is, is that the dealer has allowed them to direct and distort his life. It could even be said that he has excluded the idea of God *as cause of the storm* from his system—or because of the system; significantly, he never mentions God, but seems to regard the phenomenon of lightning as a danger dissociated from any kind of divinity, though he says that a cloud will sometimes *"select"* a six-foot man as its lightning conductor. Yet when he insists that *"Mine* is the only true rod" he exhibits the conviction of the religious fanatic; and both he and the narrator use religious terms in condemning each other: "You are profane in this time of terror"; "Impious wretch! . . . I will publish your infidel notions"; "Who has empowered you . . . to peddle round your indulgences from divine ordinations?"

The narrator's position differs from the dealer's not so much in the matter of God's and nature's destructive power as in the belief that such precautions as those the dealer takes are superstitions which amount to a systematizing of fear, that this fear separates men from one another, and that man can rest easily within the destructive framework of God and nature. The narrator's final speech to the dealer ridicules his efforts to "avert the supernal bolt": "you mere man who come here to put you and your pipe-stem between clay and sky . . ." The efforts of the dealer are powerless against the power of God; the dealer is thus a "false negotiator." We are not told what it would take to make a "true negotiator." Perhaps negotiation is impossible: between the "clay and sky" there is only the recourse of trust. "The hairs of our heads are numbered, and the days of our lives. In thunder as in sunshine, I stand at ease in the hands of my God . . . and in the blue heavens I read in the rainbow, that the Deity will not, of purpose, make war on man's earth." Perhaps it is in this notion of God being in control of destruction that the difference between the two views resides: the narrator can rely upon a benevolence, the dealer can rely only on chaos.

These two views are not set forth with any fullness; nor with much clarity of language. Because of this, some objections arise to the narrator's position. Though the Deity will not make war on purpose, will he make it accidentally? And could not the destruction of lightning be called war—a war metaphorically conveyed in the opening paragraph? Is lightning an accident, not to be seen as the work of the Creator? If so, then how can the rainbow be the sign of an armistice between God and man or between God and the earth? True, the narrator's house is unharmed; but *all* houses aren't; the narrator's rainbow is somebody else's blasted barn.

These questions do not, however, alter the fact that the narrator and the lightning-rod dealer view the world in different ways: one giving in to fears of destruction and making out of them a system of precautions that dehumanize him, the other dealing with the fact of possible destruction by trusting in a God who, seemingly, has man's well-being in mind. The two views are incompletely presented, and they only *suggest* religious systems without specifically naming them; but the suggestion is perhaps enough; and judgment can be made not on the basis of doctrine but on the basis of the way of life that results from the two views. For the lightning-rod man there is the urgent absorption in taboos and restrictions—a life of negatives that limit him to a single charmed spot in a house, unless the "wand" has been waved to secure dispensation. For the narrator there is the near-enjoyment of the spectacle of nature, a trust in some coherent power behind this spectacle, and the security that this creates. The difference, as it is expressed in behavior, is that between a life pinched and narrowed by fears and superstitious observances, and one open in its movement and possibilities. Nature as a fact—destruction in several forms—perhaps stands solidly behind *both* views: but the freedom granted by those views is decidedly more generous in one than in the other.

At the conclusion of the story the generality and lack of clarity which make these two angles of vision somewhat enigmatic are set aside—or ignored—in favor of a metaphor which condenses their meaning. The stranger's face blackens; he foams; the "indigo circles" round his eyes get larger, like "storm-rings round the midnight moon." He once again embodies the storm, its destruction, the fears and restrictions that attend it. And he is ejected from the narrator's house to drive his trade with other fearful people. This occurs while, outside, the "rainbow beamed." The rainbow—safety, promise, peace between God and "man's earth"—is the message received and accepted by the narrator. Seen fully, this metaphor is a comparison between ways of life and the skies under which we live: one rains down dangers which are met with dehumanizing superstitions and precautions; the other is open, aglow, allowing freedom, securing ease. Like many of Melville's figures, this makes a poetic sense but will not stand up under extended logical analysis. But poetry isn't an instrument of logic, and perhaps the reason that "The Lightning-Rod Man" is so unsatisfactory as a story is that it is primarily a poem.

QUESTIONS

1. As in all parables, this one is open to various interpretations, the religious being one, the strictly social (two attitudes toward life) being another. It is possible to interpret "The Lightning-Rod Man" as a parable dealing with two kinds of religious attitudes (see the analysis by Harry B. Wilson), that dramatized by the "salesman" and that by the narrator. What *specifically* is the salesman's attitude toward his divinity? Account for his "selling" his product. What religious attitude does the narrator represent? Quote detailed textural proof in your answer.

2. On the level of plot alone, "The Lightning-Rod Man" implies a greater importance than a mere realistic incident. Two people or two attitudes toward life, man, and nature come into conflict. Define these attitudes as minutely and exactly as you can. Which view of life does Melville make triumphant? Could you conjecture why he does this?

3. Some of the authors in this book have suggested that often a traditional reference (myth, symbol, Biblical parable) outside the story itself but alluded to in the story (see the analysis of "The Secret Sharer") will contribute to the meaning of the story and enrich your experience with it. Does it deepen your understanding of Melville's intentions to know of the two types of "rods" employed in the Bible: the iron rod of punishment and death and the propitious rod of healing, comfort, and love? (See Psalms 2.9, 23.4; Proverbs 22.8; Isaiah 11.1-4; Lamentations 3.1; 1 Corinthians 4.21; Revelations 2.27, 19.15.) Generally speaking, the Old Testament represents the rod of punishment and the New Testament the rod of comfort and forgiveness. Does this fact contribute to your interpretation of the story?

4. Is there any significance in the narrator's referring to the salesman's rod as a "walking stick" and a "staff"? Why does this salesman ply his trade only during storms? The lightning-rod man refers to his business as a "calling." What significance does Melville wish us to see in that word? Or in the "indigo halos" about his eyes?

5. What one statement of the narrator sums up his attitude toward Providence? It sounds as though it might have been quoted from the Psalms or Proverbs, although it is apparently Melville's invention. You will be rewarded, however, by checking Biblical references to "the hairs of our heads are numbered" the symbolic "rainbow," "scroll," and "sceptre," and the Deity's "making war on man's earth." (In the library you will find *Crudens Complete Concordance* to the Bible which will help you locate the significant passages.)

6. Attempt an analysis of "The Lightning-Rod Man" using the method employed in analyzing "The Sire de Malétroit's Door."

II

The Legend of Sleepy Hollow

Found Among the Papers of the Late Diedrich Knickerbocker

WASHINGTON IRVING

A pleasing land of drowsy head it was,
 Of dreams that wave before the half-shut eye;
And of gay castles in the clouds that pass,
 For ever flushing round a summer sky.
                              CASTLE OF INDOLENCE

In the bosom of one of those spacious coves which indent the eastern shore of the Hudson, at that broad expansion of the river denominated by the ancient Dutch navigators the Tappan Zee, and where they always prudently shortened sail, and implored the protection of St. Nicholas when they crossed, there lies a small market town or rural port, which by some is called Greensburgh, but which is more generally and properly known by the name of Tarry Town. This name was given, we are told, in former days, by the good housewives of the adjacent country, from the inveterate propensity of their husbands to linger about the village tavern on market days. Be that as it may, I do not vouch for the fact, but merely advert to it, for the sake of being precise and authentic. Not far from this village, perhaps about two miles, there is a little valley, or rather lap of land, among high hills, which is one of the quietest places in the whole world. A small brook glides through it, with just murmur enough to lull one to repose; and the occasional whistle of a quail or tapping of a woodpecker is almost the only sound that ever breaks in upon the uniform tranquillity.

I recollect that, when a stripling, my first exploit in squirrel shooting was in a grove of tall walnut trees that shades one side of the valley. I had wandered into it at noontime, when all nature is peculiarly quiet, and was startled by the roar of my own gun, as it broke the Sabbath stillness around, and was prolonged and reverberated by the angry echoes. If ever I should wish for a retreat, whither I might steal from the world and its distractions and dream quietly away the remnant of a troubled life, I know of none more promising than this little valley.

From the listless repose of the place, and the peculiar character of its inhabitants, who are descendants from the original Dutch settlers, this sequestered glen has long been known by the name of SLEEPY HOLLOW, and its rustic lads are called the Sleepy Hollow Boys throughout all the neighboring country. A drowsy, dreamy influence seems to hang over the land, and to pervade the very atmosphere. Some say that the place was bewitched by a high German doctor during the early days of the settlement; others, that an old Indian chief, the prophet or wizard of his tribe, held his powwows there before the country was discovered by Master Hendrick Hudson. Certain it is, the place still continues under the sway of some witching power that holds a spell over the minds of the good people, causing them to walk in a continual reverie. They are given to all kinds of marvelous beliefs, are subject to trances and visions, and frequently see strange sights, and hear music and voices in the air. The whole neighborhood abounds with local tales, haunted spots, and twilight superstitions; stars shoot and meteors glare oftener across the valley than in any other part of the country, and the nightmare, with her whole ninefold, seems to make it the favorite scene of her gambols.

The dominant spirit, however, that haunts this enchanted region and seems to be commander-in-chief of all the powers of the air is the apparition of a figure on horseback without a head. It is said by some to be the ghost of a Hessian trooper, whose head had been carried away by a cannon ball, in some nameless battle during the Revolutionary War, and who is ever and anon seen by the country folk, hurrying along in the gloom of night, as if on the wings of the wind. His haunts are not confined to the valley, but extend at times to the adjacent roads, and especially to the vicinity of a church at no great distance. Indeed, certain of the most authentic historians of those parts, who have been careful in collecting and collating the floating facts concerning this specter, allege that the body of the trooper, having been buried in the churchyard, the ghost rides forth to the scene of battle in nightly quest of his head; and that the rushing speed with which he sometimes passes along the Hollow, like a midnight blast, is owing to his being belated, and in a hurry to get back to the churchyard before daybreak.

Such is the general purport of this legendary superstition, which has furnished materials for many a wild story in that region of shadows; and the specter is known, at all the country firesides, by the name of the Headless Horseman of Sleepy Hollow.

It is remarkable that the visionary propensity I have mentioned is not confined to the native inhabitants of the valley, but is unconsciously imbibed by everyone who resides there for a time. However wide awake they may have been before they entered that sleepy region, they are sure, in a little time, to inhale the witching influence of the air, and begin to grow imaginative—to dream dreams and see apparitions.

I mention this peaceful spot with all possible laud; for it is in such little retired Dutch valleys, found here and there embosomed in the great State of New York, that population, manners, and customs remain fixed; while the great torrent of migration and improvement, which is making such incessant changes in other parts of this restless country, sweeps by them unobserved. They are like those little nooks of still water which border a rapid stream, where we may see the straw and bubble riding quietly at anchor, or slowly revolving in their mimic harbor, undisturbed by the rush of the passing current. Though many years have elapsed since I trod the drowsy shades of Sleepy Hollow, yet I question whether I should not still find the same trees and the same families vegetating in its sheltered bosom.

In this by-place of nature there abode, in a remote period of American history, that is to say, some thirty years since, a worthy wight of the name of Ichabod Crane, who sojourned, or, as he expressed it, "tarried," in Sleepy Hollow, for the purpose of instructing the children of the vicinity. He was a native of Connecticut, a State which supplies the nation with pioneers for the mind as well as for the forest, and sends forth yearly its legions of frontier woodsmen and country schoolmasters. The cognomen of Crane was not inapplicable to his person. He was tall, but exceedingly lank, with narrow shoulders, long arms and legs, hands that dangled a mile out of his sleeves, feet that might have served for shovels, and his whole frame most loosely hung together. His head was small, and flat at top, with huge ears, large green glassy eyes, and a long snipe nose, so that it looked like a weathercock, perched upon his spindle neck, to tell which way the wind blew. To see him striding along the profile of a hill on a windy day, with his clothes bagging and fluttering about him, one might have mistaken him for the genius of famine descending upon the earth, or some scarecrow eloped from a cornfield.

His schoolhouse was a low building of one large room, rudely constructed of logs, the windows partly glazed, and partly patched with leaves of old copybooks. It was most ingeniously secured at vacant hours by a withe twisted in the handle of the door and stakes set against the window shutters, so that, though a thief might get in with perfect ease, he would find some embarrassment in getting out; an idea most probably borrowed by the architect, Yost Van Houten, from the mystery of an eel pot. The schoolhouse stood in a rather lonely but pleasant situation, just at the foot of a woody hill, with a brook running close by, and a formidable birch tree growing at one end of it. From hence the low murmur of his pupils' voices, conning over their lessons, might be heard in a drowsy summer's day, like the hum of a beehive, interrupted now and then by the authoritative voice of the master, in the tone of menace or command, or, peradventure, by the appalling sound of the birch, as he urged some tardy loiterer along the flowery path of knowledge. Truth to say, he was a conscientious man, and ever bore in mind the golden maxim, "Spare the rod and spoil the child." Ichabod Crane's scholars certainly were not spoiled.

I would not have it imagined, however, that he was one of those cruel potentates of the school who joy in the smart of their subjects; on the contrary, he administered justice with discrimination rather than severity, taking the burthen off the backs of the weak, and laying it on those of the strong. Your mere puny stripling that winced at the least flourish of the rod was passed by with indulgence; but the claims of justice were satisfied by inflicting a double portion on some little, tough, wrong-headed, broad-skirted Dutch urchin, who sulked and swelled and grew dogged and sullen beneath the birch. All this he called "doing his duty by their parents"; and he never inflicted a chastisement without following it by the assurance, so consolatory to the smarting urchin, that "he would remember it, and thank him for it the longest day he had to live."

When school hours were over, he was even the companion and playmate of the larger boys; and on holiday afternoons would convoy some of the smaller ones home, who happened to have pretty sisters, or good housewives for mothers, noted for the comforts of the cupboard. Indeed it behooved him to keep on good terms with his pupils. The revenue arising from his school was small, and would have been scarcely sufficient to furnish him with daily bread, for he was a huge feeder, and though lank, had the dilating powers of an anaconda; but to help out his maintenance, he was, according to country custom in those parts, boarded and lodged at the houses of the farmers whose children he instructed. With these he lived successively a week at a time; thus going the rounds of the neighborhood, with all his worldly effects tied up in a cotton handkerchief.

That all this might not be too onerous on the purses of his rustic patrons, who are apt to consider the costs of schooling a grievous burden and schoolmasters as mere drones, he had various ways of rendering himself both useful and agreeable. He assisted the farmers occasionally in the lighter labors of their farms, helped to make hay, mended the fences, took the horses to water, drove the cows from pasture, and cut wood for the winter fire. He laid aside, too, all the dominant dignity and ab-

solute sway with which he lorded it in his little empire, the
school, and became wonderfully gentle and ingratiating. He
found favor in the eyes of the mothers by petting the children,
particularly the youngest; and like the lion bold, which whilom
so magnanimously the lamb did hold, he would sit with a child
on one knee, and rock a cradle with his foot for whole hours together.

In addition to his other vocations, he was the singing master
of the neighborhood, and picked up many bright shillings by
instructing the young folks in psalmody. It was a matter of no
little vanity to him, on Sundays, to take his station in front of
the church gallery, with a band of chosen singers; where, in his
own mind, he completely carried away the psalm from the parson. Certain it is, his voice resounded far above all the rest of
the congregation; and there are peculiar quavers still to be
heard in that church, and which may even be heard half a mile
off, quite to the opposite side of the millpond, on a still Sunday
morning, which are said to be legitimately descended from the
nose of Ichabod Crane. Thus, by diverse little makeshifts in
that ingenious way which is commonly denominated "by hook
and by crook," the worthy pedagogue got on tolerably enough,
and was thought, by all who understood nothing of the labor of
headwork, to have a wonderfully easy life of it.

The schoolmaster is generally a man of some importance in
the female circle of a rural neighborhood, being considered a
kind of idle gentlemanlike personage, of vastly superior taste
and accomplishments to the rough country swains, and, indeed,
inferior in learning only to the parson. His appearance, therefore, is apt to occasion some little stir at the tea table of a farmhouse, and the addition of a supernumerary dish of cakes or
sweetmeats, or, peradventure, the parade of a silver teapot. Our
man of letters, therefore, was peculiarly happy in the smiles of
all the country damsels. How he would figure among them in
the churchyard, between services on Sundays! gathering grapes
for them from the wild vines that overrun the surrounding
trees, reciting for their amusement all the epitaphs on the
tombstones, or sauntering, with a whole bevy of them, along the
banks of the adjacent millpond, while the more bashful coun-

try bumpkins hung sheepishly back, envying his superior elegance and address.

From his half-itinerant life, also, he was a kind of traveling gazette, carrying the whole budget of local gossip from house to house, so that his appearance was always greeted with satisfaction. He was, moreover, esteemed by the women as a man of great erudition, for he had read several books quite through, and was a perfect master of Cotton Mather's *History of New England Witchcraft,* in which, by the way, he most firmly and potently believed.

He was, in fact, an odd mixture of small shrewdness and simple credulity. His appetite for the marvelous, and his powers of digesting it, were equally extraordinary; and both had been increased by his residence in this spellbound region. No tale was too gross or monstrous for his capacious swallow. It was often his delight, after his school was dismissed in the afternoon, to stretch himself on the rich bed of clover, bordering the little brook that whimpered by his schoolhouse, and there con over old Mather's direful tales, until the gathering dusk of the evening made the printed page a mere mist before his eyes. Then, as he wended his way, by swamp and stream and awful woodland, to the farmhouse where he happened to be quartered, every sound of nature, at that witching hour, fluttered his excited imagination: the moan of the whippoorwill* from the hillside; the boding cry of the tree toad, that harbinger of storm; the dreary hooting of the screech owl, or the sudden rustling in the thicket of birds frightened from their roost. The fireflies, too, which sparkled most vividly in the darkest places, now and then startled him, as one of uncommon brightness would stream across his path; and if, by chance, a huge blockhead of a beetle came winging his blundering flight against him, the poor varlet was ready to give up the ghost, with the idea that he was struck with a witch's token. His only resource on such occasions, either to drown thought or drive away evil spirits, was to sing psalm tunes; and the good people of Sleepy Hollow, as they sat by their doors of an evening, were often filled with awe, at hear-

---

* The whippoorwill is a bird which is only heard at night. It receives its name from its note, which is thought to resemble those words.

ing his nasal melody, "in linked sweetness long drawn out," floating from the distant hill or along the dusky road.

Another of his sources of fearful pleasure was to pass long winter evenings with the old Dutch wives as they sat spinning by the fire, with a row of apples roasting and spluttering along the hearth, and listen to their marvelous tales of ghosts and goblins, and haunted fields, and haunted brooks, and haunted bridges, and haunted houses, and particularly of the headless horseman, or galloping Hessian of the Hollow, as they sometimes called him. He would delight them equally by his anecdotes of witchcraft, and of the direful omens and portentous sights and sounds in the air, which prevailed in the earlier times of Connecticut; and would frighten them woefully with speculations upon comets and shooting stars, and with the alarming fact that the world did absolutely turn around, and that they were half the time topsy-turvy!

But if there was a pleasure in all this, while snugly cuddling in the chimney corner of a chamber that was all of a ruddy glow from the crackling wood fire, and where, of course, no specter dared to show his face, it was dearly purchased by the terrors of his subsequent walk homewards. What fearful shapes and shadows beset his path amidst the dim and ghastly glare of a snowy night! With what wistful look did he eye every trembling ray of light streaming across the waste fields from some distant window! How often was he appalled by some shrub covered with snow, which, like a sheeted specter, beset his very path! How often did he shrink with curdling awe at the sound of his own steps on the frosty crust beneath his feet; and dread to look over his shoulder, lest he should behold some uncouth being tramping close behind him! And how often was he thrown into complete dismay by some rushing blast, howling among the trees, in the idea that it was the Galloping Hessian on one of his nightly scourings!

All these, however, were mere terrors of the night, phantoms of the mind that walk in darkness; and though he had seen many specters in his time, and been more than once beset by Satan in diverse shapes, in his lonely perambulations, yet daylight put an end to all these evils; and he would have passed a pleasant life of it, in despite of the devil and all his works, if his path had not been crossed by a being that causes more perplexity to mortal man than ghosts, goblins, and the whole race of witches put together, and that was—a woman.

Among the musical disciples who assembled, one evening in each week, to receive his instructions in psalmody, was Katrina Van Tassel, the daughter and only child of a substantial Dutch farmer. She was a blooming lass of fresh eighteen, plump as a partridge, ripe and melting and rosy-cheeked as one of her father's peaches, and universally famed, not merely for her beauty, but her vast expectations. She was withal a little of a coquette, as might be perceived even in her dress, which was a mixture of ancient and modern fashions, as most suited to set off her charms. She wore the ornaments of pure yellow gold, which her great-great-grandmother had brought over from Saardam; the tempting stomacher of the olden time; and withal a provokingly short petticoat, to display the prettiest foot and ankle in the country around.

Ichabod Crane had a soft and foolish heart toward the sex; and it is not to be wondered at that so tempting a morsel soon found favor in his eyes, more especially after he had visited her in her paternal mansion. Old Baltus Van Tassel was a perfect picture of a thriving, contented, liberal-hearted farmer. He seldom, it is true, sent either his eyes or his thoughts beyond the boundaries of his own farm; but within those everything was snug, happy, and well-conditioned. He was satisfied with his wealth, but not proud of it; and piqued himself upon the hearty abundance, rather than the style in which he lived. His stronghold was situated on the banks of the Hudson, in one of those green, sheltered, fertile nooks, in which the Dutch farmers are so fond of nestling. A great elm tree spread its broad branches over it, at the foot of which bubbled up a spring of the softest and sweetest water, in a little well, formed of a barrel, and then stole sparkling away through the grass, to a neighboring brook that bubbled along among alders and dwarf willows. Hard by the farmhouse was a vast barn that might have served for a church; every window and crevice of which seemed bursting forth with the treasures of the farm; the flail was busily re-

sounding within it from morning to night; swallows and mar-
tins skimmed twittering about the eaves; and rows of pigeons,
some with one eye turned up, as if watching the weather, some
with their heads under their wings, or buried in their bosoms,
and others swelling, and cooing, and bowing about their dames,
were enjoying the sunshine on the roof. Sleek unwieldy porkers were grunting in the repose and abundance of their pens;
whence sallied forth, now and then, troops of sucking pigs, as
if to snuff the air. A stately squadron of snowy geese were riding
in an adjoining pond, convoying whole fleets of ducks; regi-
ments of turkeys were gobbling through the farmyard, and
guinea fowls fretting about it, like ill-tempered housewives, with
their peevish discontented cry. Before the barn door strutted
the gallant cock, that pattern of a husband, a warrior, and a
fine gentleman, clapping his burnished wings and crowing in
the pride and gladness of his heart—sometimes tearing up the
earth with his feet, and then generously calling his ever-hun-
gry family of wives and children to enjoy the rich morsel which
he had discovered.

The pedagogue's mouth watered as he looked upon this
sumptuous promise of luxurious winter fare. In his devouring
mind's eye he pictured to himself every roasting pig running
about with a pudding in his belly and an apple in his mouth;
the pigeons were snugly put to bed in a comfortable pie, and
tucked in with a coverlet of crust; the geese were swimming in
their own gravy; and the ducks pairing cozily in dishes, like
snug married couples, with a decent competency of onion sauce.
In the porkers he saw carved out the future sleek side of bacon,
and juicy relishing ham; not a turkey but he beheld daintily
trussed up, with its gizzard under its wing, and, peradventure,
a necklace of savory sausages; and even bright chanticleer himself lay sprawling on his back, in a sidedish, with uplifted claws,
as if craving that quarter which his chivalrous spirit disdained
to ask while living.

As the enraptured Ichabod fancied all this, and as he rolled
his great green eyes over the fat meadow lands, the rich fields
of wheat, of rye, of buckwheat, and Indian corn, and the or-
chards burthened with ruddy fruit, which surrounded the warm

tenement of Van Tassel, his heart yearned after the damsel who was to inherit these domains, and his imagination expanded with the idea how they might be readily turned into cash, and the money invested in immense tracts of wild land, and shingle palaces in the wilderness. Nay, his busy fancy already realized his hopes, and presented to him the blooming Katrina, with a whole family of children, mounted on the top of a wagon loaded with household trumpery, with pots and kettles dangling beneath; and he beheld himself bestriding a pacing mare, with a colt at her heels, setting out for Kentucky, Tennessee, or the Lord knows where.

When he entered the house the conquest of his heart was complete. It was one of those spacious farmhouses, with high-ridged, but lowly sloping roofs, built in the style handed down from the first Dutch settlers, the low projecting eaves forming a piazza along the front, capable of being closed up in bad weather. Under this were hung flails, harness, various utensils of husbandry, and nets for fishing in the neighboring river. Benches were built along the sides for summer use; and a great spinning wheel at one end, and a churn at the other, showed the various uses to which this important porch might be devoted. From this piazza the wondering Ichabod entered the hall, which formed the center of the mansion and the place of usual residence. Here, rows of resplendent pewter, ranged on a long dresser, dazzled his eyes. In one corner stood a huge bag of wool ready to be spun; in another a quantity of linsey-woolsey just from the loom; ears of Indian corn and strings of dried apples and peaches hung in gay festoons along the walls, mingled with the gaud of red peppers; and a door left ajar gave him a peep into the best parlor, where the claw-footed chairs and dark mahogany tables shone like mirrors; and irons, with their accompanying shovel and tongs, glistened from their covert of asparagus tops; mock oranges and conch shells decorated the mantelpiece; strings of various colored birds' eggs were suspended above it; a great ostrich egg was hung from the center of the room, and a corner cupboard, knowingly left open, displayed immense treasures of old silver and well-mended china.

From the moment Ichabod laid his eyes upon these regions

of delight, the peace of his mind was at an end, and his only
study was how to gain the affections of the peerless daughter of
Van Tassel. In this enterprise, however, he had more real difficulties than generally fell to the lot of a knight-errant of yore,
who seldom had anything but giants, enchanters, fiery dragons,
and such like easily conquered adversaries to contend with; and
had to make his way merely through gates of iron and brass, and
walls of adamant, to the castle keep, where the lady of his heart
was confined; all which he achieved as easily as a man would
carve his way to the center of a Christmas pie; and then the
lady gave him her hand as a matter of course. Ichabod, on the
contrary, had to win his way to the heart of a country coquette,
beset with a labyrinth of whims and caprices, which were forever presenting new difficulties and impediments; and he had to
encounter a host of fearful adversaries of real flesh and blood,
the numerous rustic admirers, who beset every portal to her
heart, keeping a watchful and angry eye upon each other, but
ready to fly out in the common cause against any new competitor.

Among these the most formidable was a burly, roaring, roy-
stering blade, of the name of Abraham, or, according to the
Dutch abbreviation, Brom Van Brunt, the hero of the country
round, which rang with his feats of strength and hardihood. He
was broad-shouldered and double-jointed, with short curly black
hair, and a bluff but not unpleasant countenance, having a mingled air of fun and arrogance. From his Herculean frame and
great powers of limb, he had received the nickname of BROM
BONES, by which he was universally known. He was famed for
great knowledge and skill in horsemanship, being as dexterous
on horseback as a Tartar. He was foremost at all races and
cockfights; and, with the ascendency which bodily strength ac-
quires in rustic life, was the umpire in all disputes, setting his
hat on one side and giving his decisions with an air and tone ad-
mitting of no gainsay or appeal. He was always ready for either
a fight or a frolic; but had more mischief than ill will in his
composition, and, with all his overbearing roughness, there was
a strong dash of waggish good humor at bottom. He had three
or four boon companions, who regarded him as their model

and at the head of whom he scoured the country, attending every scene of feud or merriment for miles around. In cold weather he was distinguished by a fur cap, surmounted with a flaunting fox's tail; and when the folks at a country gathering descried this well-known crest at a distance, whisking about among a squad of hard riders, they always stood by for a squall. Sometimes his crew would be heard dashing along past the farmhouses at midnight, with whoop and halloo, like a troop of Don Cossacks; and the old dames, startled out of their sleep, would listen for a moment till the hurry-scurry had clattered by, and then exclaim, "Ay, there goes Brom Bones and his gang!" The neighbors looked upon him with a mixture of awe, admiration, and good will; and when any madcap prank or rustic brawl occurred in the vicinity, always shook their heads and warranted Brom Bones was at the bottom of it.

This rantipole hero had for some time singled out the blooming Katrina for the object of his uncouth gallantries, and though his amorous toying were something like the gentle caresses and endearments of a bear, yet it was whispered that she did not altogether discourage his hopes. Certain it is, his advances were signals for rival candidates to retire, who felt no inclination to cross a lion in his amours; insomuch, that when his horse was seen tied to Van Tassel's paling, on a Sunday night, a sure sign that his master was courting, or, as it is termed, "sparking," within, all other suitors passed by in despair, and carried the war into other quarters.

Such was the formidable rival with whom Ichabod Crane had to contend, and, considering all things, a stouter man than he would have shrunk from the competition, and a wiser man would have despaired. He had, however, a happy mixture of pliability and perseverance in his nature; he was in form and spirit like a supple jack—yielding, but tough; though he bent, he never broke; and though he bowed beneath the slightest pressure, yet, the moment it was away—jerk! he was as erect, and carried his head as high as ever.

To have taken the field openly against his rival would have been madness, for he was not a man to be thwarted in his amours, any more than that stormy lover Achilles. Ichabod, therefore, made his advances in a quiet and gently insinuating manner. Under cover of his character of singing master, he made frequent visits to the farmhouse; not that he had anything to apprehend from the meddlesome interference of parents, which is so often a stumbling block in the path of lovers. Balt Van Tassel was an easy indulgent soul; he loved his daughter better even than his pipe, and, like a reasonable man and an excellent father, let her have her way in everything. His notable little wife, too, had enough to do to attend to her housekeeping and manage her poultry; for, as she sagely observed, ducks and geese are foolish things, and must be looked after, but girls can take care of themselves. Thus while the busy dame bustled about the house, or plied her spinning wheel at one end of the piazza, honest Balt would sit smoking his evening pipe at the other, watching the achievements of a little wooden warrior, who, armed with a sword in each hand, was most valiantly fighting the wind on the pinnacle of the barn. In the meantime, Ichabod would carry on his suit with the daughter by the side of the spring under the great elm, or sauntering along in the twilight, that hour so favorable to the lover's eloquence.

I profess not to know how women's hearts are wooed and won. To me they have always been matters of riddle and admiration. Some seem to have but one vulnerable point, or door of access, while others have a thousand avenues, and may be captured in a thousand different ways. It is a great triumph of skill to gain the former, but a still greater proof of generalship to maintain possession of the latter, for the man must battle for his fortress at every door and window. He who wins a thousand common hearts is therefore entitled to some renown; but he who keeps undisputed sway over the heart of a coquette is indeed a hero. Certain it is, this was not the case with the redoubtable Brom Bones; and from the moment Ichabod Crane made his advances, the interests of the former evidently declined; his horse was no longer seen tied at the palings on Sunday nights, and a deadly feud gradually arose between him and the preceptor of Sleepy Hollow.

Brom, who had a degree of rough chivalry in his nature, would fain have carried matters to open warfare, and have settled their pretensions to the lady according to the mode of those most concise and simple reasoners, the knights-errant of yore— by single combat; but Ichabod was too conscious of the superior might of his adversary to enter the lists against him. He had overheard a boast of Bones that he would "double the schoolmaster up, and lay him on a shelf of his own schoolhouse," and he was too wary to give him an opportunity. There was something extremely provoking in this obstinately pacific system; it left Brom no alternative but to draw upon the funds of rustic waggery in his disposition, and to play off boorish practical jokes upon his rival. Ichabod became the object of whimsical persecution to Bones and his gang of rough riders. They harried his hitherto peaceful domains; smoked out his singing school by stopping up the chimney; broke into the schoolhouse at night, in spite of its formidable fastenings of withe and window stakes, and turned everything topsy-turvy, so that the poor schoolmaster began to think all the witches in the country held their meetings there. But what was still more annoying, Brom took all opportunities of turning him into ridicule in presence of his mistress, and had a scoundrel dog whom he taught to whine in the most ludicrous manner, and introduced as a rival of Ichabod's to instruct her in psalmody.

In this way matters went on for sometime, without producing any material effect on the relative situation of the contending powers. On a fine autumnal afternoon, Ichabod, in pensive mood, sat enthroned on the lofty stool whence he usually watched all the concerns of his little literary realm. In his hand he swayed a ferule, that scepter of despotic power; the birch of justice reposed on three nails, behind the throne, a constant terror to evildoers; while on the desk before him might be seen sundry contraband articles and prohibited weapons, detected upon the persons of idle urchins, such as half-munched apples, popguns, whirligigs, fly cages, and whole legions of rampant little paper gamecocks. Apparently there had been some appalling act of justice recently inflicted, for his scholars were all busily intent upon their books, or slyly whispering behind them with one eye kept upon the master; and a kind of buzzing stillness reigned throughout the schoolroom. It was suddenly interrupted by the appearance of a Negro, in tow-cloth jacket and trousers, a round-crowned fragment of a hat, like the cap of Mercury, and mounted on the back of a ragged, wild, half-broken colt, which he managed with a rope by way of halter. He came clattering up to the school door with an invitation to Ichabod to attend a merrymaking or "quilting frolic" to be held that evening at Mynheer Van Tassel's; and having delivered his message with that air of importance and effort at fine language which a Negro is apt to display on petty embassies of the kind, he dashed over the brook and was seen scampering away up the hollow, full of the importance and hurry of his mission.

All was now bustle and hubbub in the late quiet schoolroom. The scholars were hurried through their lessons, without stopping at trifles; those who were nimble skipped over half with impunity, and those who were tardy had a smart application now and then in the rear to quicken their speed or help them over a tall word. Books were flung aside without being put away on the shelves, inkstands were overturned, benches thrown down, and the whole school was turned loose an hour before the usual time, bursting forth like a legion of young imps, yelping and racketing about the green, in joy at their early emancipation.

The gallant Ichabod now spent at least an extra half hour at his toilet, brushing and furbishing up his best and indeed only suit of rusty black, and arranging his looks by a bit of broken looking glass that hung up in the schoolhouse. That he might make his appearance before his mistress in the true style of a cavalier he borrowed a horse from the farmer with whom he was domiciliated, a choleric old Dutchman of the name of Hans Van Ripper, and, thus gallantly mounted, issued forth, like a knight-errant in quest of adventures. But it is meet I should, in the true spirit of romantic story, give some account of the looks and equipments of my hero and his steed. The animal he bestrode was a broken-down plow horse that had outlived almost everything but his viciousness. He was gaunt and shagged, with a ewe neck and a head like a hammer; his rusty mane and tail were tangled and knotted with burrs; one eye had lost its pupil and was glaring and spectral, but the other had the gleam of a genuine devil in it. Still he must have had fire and mettle in his day, if we may judge from the name he bore of Gunpowder. He had, in fact, been a favorite steed of his master's, the choleric Van Ripper, who was a furious rider, and had infused, very probably, some of his own spirit into the animal, for, old and broken-down as he looked, there was more of the lurking devil in him than in any young filly in the country.

Ichabod was a suitable figure for such a steed. He rode with short stirrups, which brought his knees nearly up to the pommel of the saddle; his sharp elbows stuck out like grasshoppers'; he carried his whip perpendicularly in his hand, like a scepter, and, as his horse jogged on, the motion of his arms was not unlike the flapping of a pair of wings. A small wool hat rested on the top of his nose, for so his scanty strip of forehead might be called; and the skirts of his black coat fluttered out almost to the horse's tail. Such was the appearance of Ichabod and his steed, as they shambled out of the gate of Hans Van Ripper, and it was altogether such an apparition as is seldom to be met with in broad daylight.

It was, as I have said, a fine autumnal day, the sky was clear and serene, and nature wore that rich and golden livery which we always associate with the idea of abundance. The forests had put on their sober brown and yellow, while some trees of the tenderer kind had been nipped by the frosts into brilliant dyes of orange, purple, and scarlet. Streaming files of wild ducks began to make their appearance high in the air; the bark of the squirrel might be heard from the groves of beech and hickory nuts, and the pensive whistle of the quail at intervals from the neighboring stubble field.

The small birds were taking their farewell banquets. In the fullness of their revelry, they fluttered, chirping and frolicking, from bush to bush, and tree to tree, capricious from the very profusion and variety around them. There was the honest cock robin, the favorite game of stripling sportsmen, with its loud querulous note; and the twittering blackbirds flying in sable clouds; and the golden-winged woodpecker, with his crimson crest, his broad black gorget, and splendid plumage; and the cedar bird, with its red-tipped wings and yellow-tipped tail, and its little monteiro cap of feathers; and the blue jay, that noisy coxcomb, in his gay light-blue coat and white underclothes; screaming and chattering, nodding and bobbing and bowing, and pretending to be on good terms with every songster of the grove.

As Ichabod jogged slowly on his way, his eye, ever open to every symptom of culinary abundance, ranged with delight over the treasures of jolly autumn. On all sides he beheld vast store of apples, some hanging in oppressive opulence on the trees, some gathered into baskets and barrels for the market, others heaped up in rich piles for the cider press. Farther on he beheld great fields of Indian corn, with its golden ears peeping from their leafy coverlets and holding out the promise of cakes and hasty pudding; and the yellow pumpkins lying beneath them, turning up their fair round bellies to the sun, and giving ample prospects of the most luxurious of pies; and anon he passed the fragrant buckwheat fields, breathing the odor of the beehive, and as he beheld them, soft anticipations stole over his mind of dainty slapjacks, well buttered and garnished with honey or treacle, by the delicate little dimpled hand of Katrina Van Tassel.

Thus feeding his mind with many sweet thoughts and "sugared suppositions," he journeyed along the sides of a range of hills which look out upon some of the goodliest scenes of the mighty Hudson. The sun gradually wheeled his broad disk down into the west. The wide bosom of the Tappan Zee lay motionless and glassy, excepting that here and there a gentle undulation waved and prolonged the blue shadow of the distant mountain. A few amber clouds floated in the sky, without a breath of air to move them. The horizon was of a fine golden tint, changing gradually into a pure apple green, and from that into the deep blue of the mid-heaven. A slanting ray lingered on the woody crests of the precipices that overhung some parts of the river, giving greater depth to the dark-gray and purple of their rocky sides. A sloop was loitering in the distance, dropping slowly down with the tide, her sail hanging uselessly against the mast; and as the reflection of the sky gleamed along the still water, it seemed as if the vessel was suspended in the air.

It was toward evening that Ichabod arrived at the castle of the Heer Van Tassel, which he found thronged with the pride and flower of the adjacent country. Old farmers, a spare leathern-faced race, in homespun coats and breeches, blue stockings, huge shoes, and magnificent pewter buckles. Their brisk withered little dames, in close-crimped caps, long-waisted short gowns, homespun petticoats, with scissors and pincushions and gay calico pockets hanging on the outside. Buxom lasses, almost as antiquated as their mothers, excepting where a straw hat, a fine ribbon, or perhaps a white frock gave symptoms of city innovation. The sons, in short square-skirted coats with rows of stupendous brass buttons, and their hair generally queued in the fashion of the times, especially if they could procure an eel skin for the purpose, it being esteemed throughout the country as a potent nourisher and strengthener of the hair.

Brom Bones, however, was the hero of the scene, having come to the gathering on his favorite steed Dare-devil, creature, like himself, full of mettle and mischief, and which no one but himself could manage. He was, in fact, noted for preferring vicious animals, given to all kinds of tricks, which kept the rider in constant risk of his neck, for he held a tractable well-broken horse as unworthy of a lad of spirit.

Fain would I pause to dwell upon the world of charms that burst upon the enraptured gaze of my hero as he entered the state parlor of Van Tassel's mansion. Not those of the bevy of buxom lasses, with their luxurious display of red and white, but the ample charms of a genuine Dutch country tea table, in the sumptuous time of autumn. Such heaped-up platters of cakes of various and almost indescribable kinds, known only to experienced Dutch housewives! There was the doughty doughnut, the tenderer oly koek, and the crisp and crumbling cruller; sweet cakes and shortcakes, ginger cakes and honey cakes, and the whole family of cakes. And then there were apple pies and peach pies and pumpkin pies; besides slices of ham and smoked beef; and moreover delectable dishes of preserved plums, and peachs, and pears, and quinces; not to mention broiled shad and roasted chickens; together with bowls of milk and cream, all mingled higgledy-piggledy, pretty much as I have enumerated them, with the motherly teapot sending up its clouds of vapor from the midst—Heaven bless the mark! I want breath and time to discuss this banquet as it deserves, and am too eager to get on with my story. Happily, Ichabod Crane was not in so great a hurry as his historian, but did ample justice to every dainty.

He was a kind and thankful creature whose heart dilated in proportion as his skin was filled with good cheer, and whose spirits rose with eating as some men's do with drink. He could not help, too, rolling his large eyes around him as he ate, and chuckling with the possibility that he might one day be lord of all this scene of almost unimaginable luxury and splendor. Then, he thought, how soon he'd turn his back upon the old schoolhouse; snap his fingers in the face of Hans Van Ripper, and every other niggardly patron, and kick any itinerant pedagogue out of doors that should dare to call him comrade!

Old Baltus Van Tassel moved about among his guests with a face dilated with content and good humor, round and jolly as the harvest moon. His hospitable attentions were brief, but expressive, being confined to a shake of the hand, a slap on the shoulder, a loud laugh, and a pressing invitation to "fall to, and help themselves."

And now the sound of the music from the common room, or hall, summoned to the dance. The musician was an old gray-headed Negro, who had been the itinerant orchestra of the neighborhood for more than half a century. His instrument was as old and battered as himself. The greater part of the time he scraped on two or three strings, accompanying every movement of the bow with a motion of the head; bowing almost to the ground and stamping with his foot whenever a fresh couple were to start.

Ichabod prided himself upon his dancing as much as upon his vocal powers. Not a limb, not a fiber about him was idle; and to have seen his loosely hung frame in full motion, and clattering about the room, you would have thought Saint Vitus himself, that blessed patron of the dance, was figuring before you in person. He was the admiration of all the Negroes, who, having gathered, of all ages and sizes, from the farm and the neighborhood, stood forming a pyramid of shining black faces at every door and window, gazing with delight at the scene, rolling their white eyeballs, and showing grinning rows of ivory from ear to ear. How could the flogger of urchins be otherwise than animated and joyous? The lady of his heart was his partner in the dance, and smiling graciously in reply to all his amorous oglings, while Brom Bones, sorely smitten with love and jealousy, sat brooding by himself in one corner.

When the dance was at an end, Ichabod was attracted to a knot of the sager folks, who, with old Van Tassel, sat smoking at one end of the piazza, gossiping over former times, and drawing out long stories about the war.

This neighborhood, at the time of which I am speaking, was one of those highly favored places which abound with chronicle and great men. The British and American line had run near it during the war; it had, therefore, been the scene of marauding, and infested with refugees, cowboys, and all kinds of border chivalry. Just sufficient time had elapsed to enable each story-teller to dress up his tale with a little becoming fiction, and, in the indistinctness of his recollection, to make himself the hero of every exploit.

There was the story of Doffue Martling, a large blue-bearded Dutchman, who had nearly taken a British frigate with an old iron nine-pounder from a mud breastwork, only that his gun burst at the sixth discharge. And there was an old gentleman who shall be nameless, being too rich a mynheer to be lightly mentioned, who, in the Battle of White Plains, being an excellent master of defense, parried a musket ball with a small sword, insomuch that he absolutely felt it whiz around the blade and glance off at the hilt, in proof of which he was ready at any time to show the sword, with the hilt a little bent. There were several more that had been equally great in the field, not one of whom but was persuaded that he had a considerable hand in bringing the war to a happy termination.

But all these were nothing to the tales of ghosts and apparitions that succeeded. The neighborhood is rich in legendary treasures of the kind. Local tales and superstitions thrive best in these sheltered long-settled retreats, but are trampled under foot by the shifting throng that forms the population of most of our country places. Besides, there is no encouragement for ghosts in most of our villages, for they have scarcely had time to finish their first nap and turn themselves in their graves before their surviving friends have traveled away from the neighborhood; so that when they turn out at night to walk their rounds they have no acquaintance left to call upon. This is perhaps the reason why we so seldom hear of ghosts except in our long-established Dutch communities.

The immediate cause, however, of the prevalence of supernatural stories in these parts was doubtless owing to the vicinity of Sleepy Hollow. There was a contagion in the very air that blew from that haunted region; it breathed forth an atmosphere of dreams and fancies infecting all the land. Several of the Sleepy Hollow people were present at Van Tassel's, and, as usual, were doling out their wild and wonderful legends. Many dismal tales were told about funeral trains, and mourning cries and wailings heard and seen about the great tree where the unfortunate Major André was taken, and which stood in the neighborhood. Some mention was made also of the woman in white that haunted the dark glen at Raven Rock, and was often heard to shriek on winter nights before a storm, having perished there in the snow. The chief part of the stories, however, turned upon the favorite specter of Sleepy Hollow, the headless horseman, who had been heard several times of late, patrolling the country, and, it was said, tethered his horse nightly among the graves in the churchyard.

The sequestered situation of this church seems always to have made it a favorite haunt of troubled spirits. It stands on a knoll, surrounded by locust trees and lofty elms, from among which its decent whitewashed walls shine modestly forth, like Christian purity beaming through the shades of retirement. A gentle slope descends from it to a silver sheet of water, bordered by high trees, between which peeps may be caught at the blue hills of the Hudson. To look upon its grass-grown yard, where the sunbeams seem to sleep so quietly, one would think that there at least the dead might rest in peace. On one side of the church extends a wide woody dell, along which raves a large brook among broken rocks and trunks of fallen trees. Over a deep black part of the stream, not far from the church, was formerly thrown a wooden bridge; the road that led to it, and the bridge itself, were thickly shaded by overhanging trees, which cast a gloom about it, even in the daytime, but occasioned a fearful darkness at night. This was one of the favorite haunts of the headless horseman, and the place where he was most frequently encountered. The tale was told of old Brouwer, a most heretical disbeliever in ghosts, how he met the horseman returning from his foray into Sleepy Hollow, and was obliged to get up behind him; how they galloped over bush and brake, over hill and swamp, until they reached the bridge, when the horseman suddenly turned into a skeleton, threw old Brouwer into the brook, and sprang away over the treetops with a clap of thunder.

This story was immediately matched by a thrice marvelous adventure of Brom Bones, who made light of the galloping Hessian as an arrant jockey. He affirmed that, on returning one night from the neighboring village of Sing Sing, he had been overtaken by this midnight trooper; that he had offered to race with him for a bowl of punch, and should have won it too, for Daredevil beat the goblin horse all hollow, but, just as they came to the church bridge, the Hessian bolted and vanished in a flash of fire.

All these tales, told in that drowsy undertone with which men talk in the dark, the countenances of the listeners only now and then receiving a casual gleam from the glare of a pipe, sank deep in the mind of Ichabod. He repaid them in kind with large extracts from his invaluable author, Cotton Mather, and added many marvelous events that had taken place in his native State of Connecticut, and fearful sights which he had seen in his nightly walks about Sleepy Hollow.

The revel now gradually broke up. The old farmers gathered together their families in their wagons, and were heard for some time rattling along the hollow roads and over the distant hills. Some of the damsels mounted on pillions behind their favorite swains, and their lighthearted laughter, mingling with the clatter of hoofs, echoed along the silent woodlands, sounding fainter and fainter until they gradually died away—and the late scene of noise and frolic was all silent and deserted. Ichabod only lingered behind, according to the custom of country lovers, to have a tête-à-tête with the heiress, fully convinced that he was now on the high road to success. What passed at this interview I will not pretend to say, for in fact I do not know. Something, however, I fear me, must have gone wrong, for he certainly sallied forth, after no very great interval, with an air quite desolate and chopfallen. Oh these women! these women! Could that girl have been playing off any of her coquettish tricks? Was her encouragement of the poor pedagogue all a mere sham to secure her conquest of his rival? Heaven only knows, not I! Let it suffice to say, Ichabod stole forth with the air of one who had been sacking a hen roost rather than a fair lady's heart. Without looking to the right or left to notice the scene of rural wealth, on which he had so often gloated, he went straight to the stable, and with several hearty cuffs and kicks roused his steed most uncourteously from the comfortable quarters in which he was soundly sleeping, dreaming of mountains of corn and oats, and whole valleys of timothy and clover.

It was the very witching time of night that Ichabod, heavy-hearted and crestfallen, pursued his travel homeward, along the sides of the lofty hills which rise above Tarry Town, and which he had traversed so cheerily in the afternoon. The hour was as dismal as himself. Far below him, the Tappan Zee spread its dusky and indistinct waste of waters, with here and there the tall mast of a sloop, riding quietly at anchor under the land. In the dead hush of midnight he could even hear the barking of the watchdog from the opposite shore of the Hudson, but it was so vague and faint as only to give an idea of his distance from this faithful companion of man. Now and then, too, the long-drawn crowing of a cock, accidentally awakened, would sound far, far off, from some farmhouse away among the hills—but it was like a dreaming sound in his ear. No signs of life occurred near him, but occasionally the melancholy chirp of a cricket, or perhaps the guttural twang of a bullfrog, from a neighboring marsh, as if sleeping uncomfortably and turning suddenly in his bed.

All the stories of ghosts and goblins that he had heard in the afternoon now came crowding upon his recollection. The night drew darker and darker; the stars seemed to sink deeper in the sky, and driving clouds occasionally hid them from his sight. He had never felt so lonely and dismal. He was, moreover, approaching the very place where many of the scenes of the ghost stories had been laid. In the center of the road stood an enormous tulip tree, which towered like a giant above all the other trees of the neighborhood and formed a kind of landmark. Its limbs were gnarled and fantastic, large enough to form trunks for ordinary trees, twisting down almost to the earth and rising again into the air. It was connected with the tragical story of the unfortunate André, who had been taken prisoner hard by; and was universally known by the name of Major André's tree. The common people regarded it with a mixture of respect and superstition, partly out of sympathy for the fate of its ill-starred namesake, and partly from the tales of strange sights and doleful lamentations told concerning it.

As Ichabod approached this fearful tree, he began to whistle; he thought his whistle was answered—it was but a blast sweeping sharply through the dry branches. As he approached a little nearer, he thought he saw something white hanging in the midst of the tree—he paused and ceased whistling; but on looking more narrowly, perceived that it was a place where the tree had been scathed by lightning and the white wood laid bare. Suddenly he heard a groan—his teeth chattered and his knees smote against the saddle; it was but the rubbing of one huge bough upon another as they were swayed about by the breeze. He passed the tree in safety, but new perils lay before him.

About two hundred yards from the tree a small brook crossed the road and ran into a marshy and thickly wooded glen, known by the name of Wiley's swamp. A few rough logs, laid side by side, served for a bridge over this stream. On that side of the road where the brook entered the wood, a group of oaks and chestnuts, matted thick with wild grapevines, threw a cavernous gloom over it. To pass this bridge was the severest trial. It was at this identical spot that the unfortunate André was captured, and under the covert of those chestnuts and vines were the sturdy yeomen concealed who surprised him. This has ever since been considered a haunted stream, and fearful are the feelings of the schoolboy who has to pass it alone after dark.

As he approached the stream his heart began to thump; he summoned up, however, all his resolution, gave his horse half a score of kicks in the ribs, and attempted to dash briskly across the bridge; but instead of starting forward, the perverse old animal made a lateral movement and ran broadside against the fence. Ichabod, whose fears increased with the delay, jerked the reins on the other side, and kicked lustily with the contrary foot; it was all in vain; his steed started, it is true, but it was only to plunge to the opposite side of the road into a thicket of brambles and alder bushes. The schoolmaster now bestowed both whip and heel upon the starveling ribs of old Gunpowder, who dashed forward, snuffling and snorting, but came to a stand just by the bridge with a suddenness that had nearly sent his rider sprawling over his head. Just at this moment a plashy tramp by the side of the bridge caught the sensitive ear of Ichabod. In the dark shadow of the grove, on the margin of the brook, he beheld something huge, misshapen, black and towering. It stirred not, but seemed gathered up in the gloom, like some gigantic monster ready to spring upon the traveler.

The hair of the affrighted pedagogue rose upon his head with terror. What was to be done? To turn and fly was now too late; and besides, what chance was there of escaping ghost or goblin, if such it was, which could ride upon the wings of the wind? Summoning up, therefore, a show of courage, he demanded in stammering accents—"Who are you?" He received no reply. He repeated his demand in a still more agitated voice. Still there was no answer. Once more he cudgeled the sides of the inflexible Gunpowder, and, shutting his eyes, broke forth with involuntary fervor into a psalm tune. Just then the shadowy object of alarm put itself in motion, and, with a scramble and a bound, stood at once in the middle of the road. Though the night was dark and dismal, yet the form of the unknown might now in some degree be ascertained. He appeared to be a horseman of large dimensions, and mounted on a black horse of powerful frame. He made no offer of molestation or sociability, but kept aloof on one side of the road, jogging along on the blind side of old Gunpowder, who had now got over his fright and waywardness.

Ichabod, who had no relish for this strange midnight companion, and bethought himself of the adventure of Brom Bones with the Galloping Hessian, now quickened his steed, in hopes of leaving him behind. The stranger, however, quickened his horse to an equal pace. Ichabod pulled up, and fell into a walk, thinking to lag behind—the other did the same. His heart began to sink within him; he endeavored to resume his psalm tune, but his parched tongue clove to the roof of his mouth, and he could not utter a stave. There was something in the moody and dogged silence of this pertinacious companion that was mysterious and appalling. It was soon fearfully accounted for. On mounting a rising ground, which brought the figure of his fellow-traveler in relief against the sky, gigantic in height, and muffled in a cloak, Ichabod was horror-struck on perceiving that he was headless! But his horror was still more increased on observing that the head, which should have rested on his shoulders, was carried before him on the pommel of the saddle. His terror rose to desperation; he rained a shower of kicks and blows upon Gunpowder, hoping, by a sudden movement, to give his companion the slip—but the specter started full jump with him. Away then they dashed, through thick and thin, stones flying and sparks flashing at every bound. Ichabod's flimsy garments fluttered in the air as he stretched his long lank body away over his horse's head, in the eagerness of his flight.

They had now reached the road which turns off to Sleepy Hollow; but Gunpowder, who seemed possessed with a demon, instead of keeping up it, made an opposite turn, and plunged headlong downhill to the left. This road leads through a sandy hollow, shaded by trees for about a quarter of a mile, where it crosses the bridge famous in goblin story, and just beyond swells the green knoll on which stands the whitewashed church.

As yet the panic of the steed has given his unskillful rider an apparent advantage in the chase; but just as he had got halfway through the hollow, the girths of the saddle gave way, and he felt it slipping from under him. He seized it by the pommel and endeavored to hold it firm, but in vain; and had just time to save himself by clasping old Gunpowder around the neck when the saddle fell to the earth, and he heard it trampled under foot by his pursuer. For a moment the terror of Hans Van Ripper's wrath passed across his mind—for it was his Sunday saddle; but this was no time for petty fears; the goblin was hard on his haunches, and (unskillful rider that he was!) he had much ado to maintain his seat, sometimes slipping on one side, sometimes on the other, and sometimes jolted on the high ridge of his horse's backbone with a violence that he verily feared would cleave him asunder.

An opening in the trees now cheered him with the hopes that the church bridge was at hand. The wavering reflection of a silver star in the bosom of the brook told him that he was not mistaken. He saw the walls of the church dimly glaring under the trees beyond. He recollected the place where Brom Bones's ghostly competitor had disappeared. "If I can but reach that bridge," thought Ichabod, "I am safe." Just then he heard the black steed panting and blowing close behind him; he even fancied that he felt his hot breath. Another convulsive kick in the ribs and old Gunpowder sprang upon the bridge; he thundered over the resounding planks; he gained the opposite side; and now Ichabod cast a look behind to see if his pursuer should vanish, according to rule, in a flash of fire and brimstone. Just then he saw the goblin rising in his stirrups, and in the very act of hurling his head at him. Ichabod endeavored to dodge the horrible missile, but too late. It encountered his cranium with a tremendous crash—he was tumbled headlong into the dust, and Gunpowder, the black steed, and the goblin rider, passed by like a whirlwind.

The next morning the old horse was found without his saddle, and with the bridle under his feet, soberly cropping the grass at his master's gate. Ichabod did not make his appearance at breakfast—dinner hour came, but no Ichabod. The boys assembled at the schoolhouse, and strolled idly about the banks of the brook; but no schoolmaster. Hans Van Ripper now began to feel some uneasiness about the fate of poor Ichabod, and his saddle. An inquiry was set on foot, and after diligent investigation they came upon his traces. In one part of the road leading to the church was found the saddle trampled in the dirt; the tracks of horses' hoofs deeply dented in the road, and evidently at furious speed, were traced to the bridge, beyond which, on the bank of a broad part of the brook, where the water ran deep and black, was found the hat of the unfortunate Ichabod, and close beside it a shattered pumpkin.

The brook was searched, but the body of the schoolmaster was not to be discovered. Hans Van Ripper, as executor of his estate, examined the bundle which contained all his worldly effects. They consisted of two shirts and a half, two stocks for the neck, a pair or two of worsted stockings, an old pair of corduroy small clothes, a rusty razor, a book of psalm tunes full of dogs' ears, and a broken pitchpipe. As to the books and furniture of the schoolhouse, they belonged to the community, excepting Cotton Mather's *History of Witchcraft, a New England Almanac,* and a book of dreams and fortune-telling; in which last was a sheet of foolscap much scribbled and blotted in several fruitless attempts to make a copy of verses in honor of the heiress of Van Tassel. These magic books and the poetic scrawl were forthwith consigned to the flames by Hans Van Ripper, who from that time forward determined to send his children no more to school, observing that he never knew any good come of this same reading and writing. Whatever money the schoolmaster possessed, and he had received his quarter's pay but a day or two before, he must have had about his person at the time of his disappearance.

The mysterious event caused much speculation at the church on the following Sunday. Knots of gazers and gossips were collected in the churchyard, at the bridge, and at the spot where the hat and pumpkin had been found. The stories of Brouwer, of Bones, and a whole budget of others were called to mind; and when they had diligently considered them all and compared them with the symptoms of the present case, they shook their heads and came to the conclusion that Ichabod had been carried off by the galloping Hessian. As he was a bachelor and in nobody's debt, nobody troubled his head any more about him. The school was removed to a different quarter of the hollow, and another pedagogue reigned in his stead.

It is true an old farmer, who had been down to New York on a visit several years after, and from whom this account of the ghostly adventure was received, brought home the intelligence that Ichabod Crane was still alive; that he had left the neighborhood, partly through fear of the goblin and Hans Van Ripper, and partly in mortification at having been suddenly dismissed by the heiress; that he had changed his quarters to a distant part of the country, had kept school and studied law at the same time, had been admitted to the bar, turned politician, electioneered, written for the newspapers, and finally had been made a justice of the Ten Pound Court. Brom Bones too, who shortly after his rival's disappearance conducted the blooming Katrina in triumph to the altar, was observed to look exceedingly knowing whenever the story of Ichabod was related, and always burst into a hearty laugh at the mention of the pumpkin, which led some to suspect that he knew more about the matter than he chose to tell.

The old country wives, however, who are the best judges of these matters, maintain to this day that Ichabod was spirited away by supernatural means; and it is a favorite story often told about the neighborhood around the winter evening fire. The bridge became more than ever an object of superstitious awe, and that may be the reason why the road has been altered of late years, so as to approach the church by the border of the millpond. The schoolhouse, being deserted, soon fell to decay, and was reported to be haunted by the ghost of the unfortunate pedagogue; and the plowboy, loitering homeward of a still summer evening, has often fancied his voice at a distance, chanting a melancholy psalm tune among the tranquil solitudes of Sleepy Hollow.

POSTSCRIPT

Found in the Handwriting of Mr. Knickerbocker

The preceding Tale is given, almost in the precise words in which I heard it related at a Corporation meeting of the ancient city of Manhattoes, at which were present many of its sagest and most illustrious burghers. The narrator was a pleasant, shabby, gentlemanly old fellow, in pepper-and-salt clothes, with a sadly humorous face, and one whom I strongly suspected of being poor—he made such efforts to be entertaining. When his story was concluded, there was much laughter and approbation, particularly from two or three deputy aldermen, who had been asleep a greater part of the time. There was, however, one tall, dry-looking old gentleman with beetling eyebrows, who maintained a grave and rather severe face throughout, now and then folding his arms, inclining his head, and looking down upon the floor, as if turning a doubt over in his mind. He was one of your wary men, who never laugh but upon good grounds—when they have reason and the law on their side. When the mirth of the rest of the company had subsided and silence was restored, he leaned one arm on the elbow of his chair, and, sticking the other akimbo, demanded, with a slight but exceedingly sage motion of the head, and contraction of the brow, what was the moral of the story, and what it went to prove?

The storyteller, who was just putting a glass of wine to his lips as a refreshment after his toils, paused for a moment, looked at his inquirer with an air of infinite deference, and, lowering the glass slowly to the table, observed that the story was intended most logically to prove:

"That there is no situation in life but has its advantages and pleasures—provided we but take a joke as we find it.

"That, therefore, he that runs races with goblin troopers is likely to have rough riding of it.

"Ergo, for a country schoolmaster to be refused the hand of a Dutch heiress is a certain step to high preferment in the state."

The cautious old gentleman knit his brows tenfold closer after this explanation, being sorely puzzled by the ratiocination of the syllogism; while, methought, the one in pepper-and-salt eyed him with something of a triumphant leer. At length, he observed, that all this was very well, but still he thought the story a little on the extravagant [side]—there were one or two points on which he had his doubts.

"Faith, sir," replied the storyteller, "as to that matter, I don't believe one-half of it myself."

D.K.

Sleepy Oppositions

IRVING MALIN

There are few studies of "The Legend of Sleepy Hollow" that do it justice. Most critics regard it as clever satire of Yankee acquisitiveness or as good "local color." It is viewed as a "forerunner" of the American short story—a bit limited, simple-minded, uncertain. But there is another way of reading the legend.

"The Legend of Sleepy Hollow" is concerned with the conflicts of life—the conflict between dream and reality, community and individuality, strength and weakness. It pictures these in melodramatic, "one-sided" ways. But it does more: it tries to present a Gothic view of life, the "horror of it all." Why then do children read the legend? Irving does not confront the oppositions with hard, adult eyes. He enchants the Gothic materials, clouding them in wish-fulfillment. He unconsciously flees from them. "The Legend of Sleepy Hollow" is thus a curious work: half-adult, half-Gothic, half-resolved. In spite of the ambivalences, perhaps because of them, we return to it. Good-natured Washington Irving is our cousin—as Allen Tate has written of Poe—although we would not admit it.

Ichabod Crane is a strange hero. He is, as Irving tells us, "an odd mixture of small shrewdness and simple credulity." The *odd mixture* is important. He is a schoolteacher but he is rather childish—he believes, for example, in "ghosts and goblins." He is somewhat effeminate—he gets along better with women than with active men. He is thin but he dreams of fecundity. He is an "animated," awkward dancer. These contraries make us laugh at him.

But Ichabod is not wholly comic. He lacks insight into himself. He does not know why he acts as he does, what others really think of him. He is imaginatively pursuing the ideal, but he does not cope with threatening reality or "superreality." He is too simple-minded to be adult, although he can manipulate others to make some dreams come true.

Note the use of oppositions: Ichabod, by being "comic" and "serious," adult and childish, dreamlike and real, forces us to have ambivalent reactions. Should we laugh? Should we sympathize with him? We aren't *sure*. Neither is the narrator. Superficially, he pokes fun at him. "To see him striding along the profile of a hill on a windy day, with his clothes bagging and fluttering about him, one might have mistaken him for the genius of famine descending upon the earth, or some scarecrow eloped from a cornfield." But he seems close to Crane's pursuit of the ideal, to his delight in music, dancing—the imagination. I maintain that the narrator is so *unsure* of the correct attitudes toward his hero that he leaves them open, much to our annoyance.

We *are* sure that we know Brom Bones. He is much less interesting because he is one-sided, healthy, stereotyped. He masters the things Ichabod neglects. We are told that he is "always ready for either a fight or a frolic"; he has "more mischief than ill will in his composition"; he is, in short, a figure of "strength and hardihood"—earthbound, active. But it is difficult to like Brom Bones. His imperfection lies in his nastiness, his carefree violence.

What we have then are two characters from different "worlds" —Ichabod lives in the world of the "spirit," of dreams; Brom is "real." The narrator forces us to choose one or the other, to "identify" with that one, as we read. Our entire attitude toward life is tied to this choice. Remember the oppositions: Ichabod is imaginative, passive, and ambivalent; Brom Bones, a kind of inverse reflection, is completely opposite. Again the narrator does not really help us to make the choice. He is as ambivalent toward Brom Bones as he is toward Ichabod Crane. He admires him as do the neighbors: "The neighbors looked upon him with a mixture of awe, admiration, and good will; and when any madcap prank or rustic brawl occurred in the vicinity, always shook their heads and warranted Brom Bones was at the bottom of it." But he also fears him and what he represents.

In Sleepy Hollow women are the prize. Katrina represents beauty, fecundity, peacefulness at home, poetic ideals, healthy love life—in other words, she is a prize on as many levels as there are in the legend. On the *artistic* level she is Ichabod's *imaginative ideal,* but she is also Brom's *earth-bound wife.* On the *sexual* level she is a kind of *mother* for Ichabod—remember his vision of her and the food!—or *sex partner* for Brom. The important thing, then, is that Katrina is the universal prize—she *offers something valuable; she* is valuable for the two men who court her.

Again ambivalence enters: Katrina is "destructive" because she forces men to fight for her—their conflicts are more "open" and powerful because of her. The narrator admits he does not know how to regard her: "—Oh these women! these women! Could that girl have been playing off any of her coquettish tricks?—Was her encouragement of the poor pedagogue all a mere sham to secure her conquest of his rival?—Heaven only knows, not I!"

Now we come to the Headless Horseman. In the world of irresolution, ambivalence, and duplicity that the narrator has been creating, the Headless Horseman is that principle which offers final destruction to Ichabod's desires. Thus he can be the image of castration: he reveals to the weak schoolmaster that he can never achieve health with Katrina; he *mirrors* his incomplete nature. He can also be the horror of the spirit world—that horror Ichabod neglects when he dreams of beauty. The Headless Horseman, being martial, is also symbolic of the real problems the "crane" has evaded—these real problems catch up to him eventually.

Even here things are left open. Ichabod *disappears.* We don't see his body; we don't see if the Horseman is real. (That Brom Bones smiles at the incident leads us to suspect *he* is the horseman, but this introduces ambiguity: Brom plays a game of the spirit; he begins to reflect Ichabod's fancies.) The horror is neglected at the end of the legend; so is explanation. We are left with the "still summer evening"—false peace covers all.

"The Legend of Sleepy Hollow" concretizes the conflicts I have discussed by means of imagery. Here is the first paragraph:

In the bosom of one of those spacious coves which indent the eastern shore of the Hudson, at that broad expansion of the river denominated by the ancient Dutch navigators the Tappan Zee, and where they always prudently shortened sail, and implored the protection of St. Nicholas when they crossed, there lies a small market town or rural port, which by some is called Greensburgh, but which is more generally and properly known by the name of Tarry Town. This name was given, we are told, in former days, by the good housewives of the adjacent country, from the inveterate propensity of their husbands to linger about the village tavern on market days. Be that as it may, I do not vouch for the fact, but merely advert to it, for the sake of being precise and authentic. Not far from this village, perhaps about two miles, there is a little valley, or rather lap of land, among high hills, which is one of the quietest places in the whole world. A small brook glides through it, with just murmur enough to lull one to repose; and the occasional whistle of a quail or tapping of a woodpecker is almost the only sound that ever breaks in upon the uniform tranquillity.

The paragraph is a psychological overture. It states many motifs which will be heard again. "Tarry Town" and "Sleepy Hollow" are resting places. In the past navigators would *stop* there. We have opposing images of "uniform tranquillity" and presumably noisy life, of voyage (often dangerous) and shelter (calm stasis). The paragraph reveals that the legend deals with the conflict between growing up and remaining still. Notice, however, how the narrator is slanting the issue. The oppositions are muted: peace or stillness is embraced, without complete investigation. The threatening voyage or noise must be avoided.

One other thing comes to the surface: the narrator says he cannot "vouch for the fact." Throughout the legend he repeats the same kind of statement. Now the admission that reality is duplicitous frightened Poe, Hawthorne, and Melville—indeed, it accounts for the terrors *we* live under. But the narrator just glances at the problem, then flees from it. He gains control and he resumes his charming, soft tone—a "drowsy, dreamy influence" seems to hang over him. It is not too risky to say that the narrator and all of the legendary people return to the womb. That is why we see the "small brook," the "lap of land," the "good housewives"—the valley mothers insecure dreamers. They sleep here.

The foregoing interpretation explains the next paragraph in "The Legend of Sleepy Hollow." The narrator recollects that once he "wandered" into the valley and was "startled by the roar of [his] gun." The roar caused "angry echoes." He states that if "ever [he] should wish for a retreat, whither [he] might steal from the world and its distractions and dream quietly away the remnant of a troubled life, [he] know[s] of none more promising than this little valley." Look closely: there is again the opposition between the world of painful reality and the valley of peaceful dream. But even in Sleepy Hollow the narrator—who I assume is Irving—cannot flee from the noise of conflict. The gun roars. Obviously the gun is phallic, but the important thing is that as voyager or hunter he should *not* be startled by it—it should be part of him. Instead, the narrator gives up his active strength, afraid of the internal echoes which command him to move. He retreats.

When the narrator relates the adventures of Ichabod Crane, he projects his desires. These desires color the legend, enchanting it. He maintains that all good people in the valley are wrapped in reverie; *they* are dreamers. The gun that threatens the dreamlike stillness is now given to the "Hessian trooper, whose head had been carried away by a cannon ball, in some nameless battle during the Revolutionary War." The Headless Horseman is the reality or "superreality" principle. He is the voyager who cannot rest in peace. Because the narrator cannot accept the conflicts of life, he is *hurt* by the horseman, *shattered by life*. Furthermore, he sees him as angry, like the previous echoes—a "dominant spirit" who can punish him for returning to the womb. Is it unreasonable to say that this "commander-in-chief" is the father, the conscience?

Now we meet Ichabod. He has "tarried" in the valley so long that he has lost all notions of self-discovery, except through reverie. He is as childlike as his students. The narrator likens him to a "scarecrow"—inhuman, never moving. Possibly there is a pun involved because the schoolmaster is "scared," afraid of reality. Although he is at home with the damsels, he is afraid of that castrating father, the *one* who knows that he has retreated from life: "How often did he shrink with curdling awe at the sound of his own steps on the frosty crust beneath his feet; and dread to look over his shoulder, lest he should behold some uncouth being trampling close behind him!"

The oppositions are apparent in the images of noise and motion, quiet and stasis, offered throughout the legend. Here are some of them: Ichabod dreams of Katrina and her father's house, as he rides to see her:

> As Ichabod jogged *slowly* on his way, his eye, ever open to every symptom of culinary abundance, *ranged with delight* over the treasurers of jolly autumn. . . . Farther on he beheld great fields of Indian corn, with its golden ears peeping from their leafy coverlets . . . ; and the yellow pumpkins *lying beneath them,* turning up their fair round bellies to the sun, and giving ample prospects of the most luxurious of pies; and anon he passed the fragrant buckwheat fields, breathing the odor of the beehive, and as he beheld them, *soft anticipations* stole over his mind of dainty slapjacks, well buttered and garnished with honey or treacle, by the delicate little dimpled hand of Katrina Van Tassel. (Author's italics.)

The scene switches to Brom; we get notions of furious activity, of "mettle and mischief." He is a completely different voyager from Ichabod. The house of Katrina is the resting place for both of them. We have a prelude to the noise at the legend's end in the good-natured frivolity of the party; music enhances the scene. (Brom Bones is associated with "whoop and hallo"; Ichabod with singing.) And the Headless Horseman's race with Brom (as he tells it) increases the noise and movement. The departure of Ichabod is still at first—no "signs of life occurred near him, but occasionally the melancholy chirp of a cricket, or perhaps the gutteral twang of a bullfrog, from a neighboring marsh, as if sleeping uncomfortably and turning suddenly in his bed." There are omens of unrest in the latter part of the sentence. Foreboding enters. Then we hear the "thump" of his heart; he attempts to "dash briskly" across the bridge, screaming "Who are you?" to the shadow near him. We see "stones flying" and "sparks flashing" as he flees. (His previous voyage to

Katrina is thus opposed; reality begins to "overturn.") The
frenzy of the scene is completely established in the following
passage:

Another convulsive kick in the ribs and old Gunpowder [*notice how-
the horse's name is restated at this crucial point*] sprang upon the bridge;
he thundered over the resounding planks; he gained the opposite side;
and now Ichabod cast a look behind to see if his pursuer should vanish,
according to rule, in a flash of fire and brimstone. Just then he saw the
goblin rising in his stirrups, and in the very act of hurling his head at
him. Ichabod endeavored to dodge the horrible missile, but too late. It
encountered his cranium with a tremendous crash—he was tumbled
headlong into the dust, and Gunpowder, the black steed, and the goblin
rider, passed by like a whirlwind.

(Unlike the "ancient Dutch navigators" mentioned at the beginning of the legend, Ichabod no longer has a resting place,
except in the dust.) The oppositions are not ended. The narrator now presents the stillness of Sleepy Hollow as Katrina and
Brom Bones marry, as the old wives and the ploughboy, "loitering homeward of a still summer evening," think about the past
pursuit of Ichabod by the Horseman. The legend ends quietly
as Irving calms the motion. "Loitering" replaces the "convulsive
kick." The old wives remain.

One word about style. Although the narrator attempts to con-
vey noisy movement, he is less adept in this respect than in pres-
entation of repose. The style insists on deliberate control, balance of phrases, slow rhythms, many adjectives—it is a perfect
instrument for muting the oppositions of life:

The school-house, being deserted, soon fell to decay, and was reported
to be haunted by the ghost of the unfortunate pedagogue; and the
ploughboy, loitering homeward of a still summer evening, has often
fancied his voice at a distance, chanting a melancholy psalm tune among
the tranquil solitudes of Sleepy Hollow.

I recommend "The Legend of Sleepy Hollow" to those adults
who want to flee from real problems of life into a world of still
summer evenings. To adults who accept the burdens of life the
legend offers a warning: *Don't retreat to the hollow.*

COMMENT

"The Legend of Sleepy Hollow" is usually looked at in terms of "local color," cozy humor, and satire of Yankee acquisitiveness. The method used here can be applied in Kafka's "A Country Doctor" and Conrad's "The Secret Sharer"—in both and some others there is the conflict between the romantic design or quest or ideal and horrifying reality. Sex is important in the stories—usually impotence; frigidity (in imagery too) is found in Hawthorne, Kafka, and Faulkner.

This essay on "The Legend of Sleepy Hollow" applies to Irving as well in "Rip Van Winkle," "Spectre Bridegroom," "Tale of the German Student," "The Arabian Astrologer" from *Alhambra,* and the history of *Columbus*—in all we have wish-fulfillment (ideal) crossed by nightmare, the breakdown of the family, doomed voyage (except "Bridegroom" and *Columbus*), passivity triumphant.

III

The Sire de Malétroit's Door

ROBERT LOUIS STEVENSON

Denis de Beaulieu was not yet two-and-twenty, but he counted himself a grown man, and a very accomplished cavalier into the bargain. Lads were early formed in that rough, warfaring epoch; and when one has been in a pitched battle and a dozen raids, has killed one's man in an honorable fashion, and knows a thing or two of strategy and mankind, a certain swagger in the gait is surely to be pardoned. He had put up his horse with due care, and supped with due deliberation; and then, in a very agreeable frame of mind, went out to pay a visit in the gray of the evening. It was not a very wise proceeding on the young man's part. He would have done better to remain beside the fire or go decently to bed. For the town was full of the troops of Burgundy and England under a mixed command; and though Denis was there on safe-conduct, his safe-conduct was like to serve him little on a chance encounter.

It was September, 1429; the weather had fallen sharp; a flighty piping wind, laden with showers, beat about the township; and the dead leaves ran riot along the streets. Here and there a window was already lighted up; and the noise of men-at-arms making merry over supper within, came forth in fits and was swallowed up and carried away by the wind. The night fell swiftly; the flag of England, fluttering on the spire-top, grew ever fainter and fainter against the flying clouds—a black speck like a swallow in the tumultuous, leaden chaos of the sky. As the night fell the wind rose, and began to hoot under archways and roar amid the tree-tops in the valley below the town.

Denis de Beaulieu walked fast and was soon knocking at his friend's door; but though he promised himself to stay only a little while and make an early return, his welcome was so pleasant, and he found so much to delay him, that it was already long past midnight before he said good-bye upon the threshold. The wind had fallen again in the meanwhile; the night was as black as the grave; not a star, nor a glimmer of moonshine, slipped through the canopy of cloud. Denis was ill-acquainted with the intricate lanes of Chateau Landon; even by daylight he had found some trouble in picking his way; and in this absolute darkness he soon lost it altogether. He was certain of one thing only—to keep mounting the hill; for his friend's house lay at the lower end, or tail, of Chateau Landon, while the inn was up at the head, under the great church spire. With this clue to go upon he stumbled and groped forward, now breathing more freely in open places where there was a good slice of sky overhead, now feeling along the wall in stifling closes. It is an eerie and mysterious position to be thus submerged in opaque blackness in an almost unknown town. The silence is terrifying in its possibilities. The touch of cold window-bars to the exploring hand startles the man like the touch of a toad; the inequalities of the pavement shake his heart into his mouth; a piece of denser darkness threatens an ambuscade or a chasm in the pathway; and where the air is brighter, the houses put on strange and bewildering appearances, as if to lead him farther from his way. For Denis, who had to regain his inn without attracting notice, there was real danger as well as mere discomfort in the walk; and he went warily and boldly at once, and at every corner paused to make an observation.

He had been for some time threading a lane so narrow that he could touch a wall with either hand when it began to open out and go sharply downward. Plainly this lay no longer in the direction of his inn; but the hope of a little more light tempted him forward to reconnoitre. The lane ended in a terrace with a bartizan wall, which gave an outlook between high houses, as out of an embrasure, into the valley lying dark and formless several hundred feet below. Denis looked down, and could discern a few tree-tops waving and a single speck of brightness where the river ran across a weir. The weather was clearing up, and the sky had lightened, so as to show the outline of the heavier clouds and the dark margin of the hills. By the uncertain glimmer, the house on his left hand should be a place of some pretensions; it was surmounted by several pinnacles and turret-tops; the round stern of a chapel, with a fringe of flying buttresses, projected boldly from the main block; and the door was sheltered under a deep porch carved with figures and overhung by two long gargoyles. The windows of the chapel gleamed through their intricate tracery with a light as of many tapers, and threw out the buttresses and the peaked roof in a more intense blackness against the sky. It was plainly the hotel of some great family of the neighborhood; and as it reminded Denis of a town house of his own at Bourges, he stood for some time gazing up at it and mentally gauging the skill of the architects and the consideration of the two families.

There seemed to be no issue to the terrace but the lane by which he had reached it; he could only retrace his steps, but he had gained some notion of his whereabouts, and hoped by this means to hit the main thoroughfare and speedily regain the inn. He was reckoning without that chapter of accidents which was to make this night memorable above all others in his career; for he had not gone back above a hundred yards before he saw a light coming to meet him, and heard loud voices speaking together in the echoing narrows of the lane. It was a party of men-at-arms going the night round with torches. Denis assured himself that they had all been making free with the wine-bowl, and were in no mood to be particular about safe-conducts or the niceties of chivalrous war. It was as like as not that they would kill him like a dog and leave him where he fell. The situation was inspiriting but nervous. Their own torches would conceal him from sight, he reflected; and he hoped that they would drown the noise of his footsteps with their own empty voices. If he were but fleet and silent, he might evade their notice altogether.

Unfortunately, as he turned to beat a retreat, his foot rolled upon a pebble; he fell against the wall with an ejaculation, and his sword rang loudly on the stones. Two or three voices demanded who went there—some in French, some in English; but Denis made no reply, and ran the faster down the lane. Once upon the terrace, he paused to look back. They still kept calling after him, and just then began to double the pace in pursuit, with a considerable clank of armor, and great tossing of the torchlight to and fro in the narrow jaws of the passage.

Denis cast a look around and darted into the porch. There he might escape observation, or—if that were too much to expect—was in a capital posture whether for parley or defence. So thinking, he drew his sword and tried to set his back against the door. To his surprise, it yielded behind his weight; and though he turned in a moment, continued to swing back on oiled and noiseless hinges, until it stood wide open on a black interior. When things fall out opportunely for the person concerned, he is not apt to be critical about the how or why, his own immediate personal convenience seeming a sufficient reason for the strangest oddities and revolutions in our sublunary things; and so Denis, without a moment's hesitation, stepped within and partly closed the door behind him to conceal his place of refuge. Nothing was further from his thoughts than to close it altogether; but for some inexplicable reason—perhaps by a spring or a weight—the ponderous mass of oak whipped itself out of his fingers and clanked to, with a formidable rumble and a noise like the falling of an automatic bar.

The round, at that very moment, debouched upon the terrace and proceeded to summon him with shouts and curses. He heard them ferreting in the dark corners; the stock of a lance even rattled along the outer surface of the door behind which he stood; but these gentlemen were in too high a humor to be long delayed, and soon made off down a corkscrew pathway which had escaped Denis's observation, and passed out of sight and hearing along the battlements of the town.

Denis breathed again. He gave them a few minutes' grace for fear of accidents, and then groped about for some means of opening the door and slipping forth again. The inner surface was quite smooth, not a handle, not a moulding, not a projection of any sort. He got his fingernails round the edges and pulled, but the mass was immovable. He shook it, it was as firm as a rock. Denis de Beaulieu frowned and gave vent to a little noiseless whistle. What ailed the door? he wondered. Why was it open? How came it to shut so easily and so effectually after him? There was something obscure and underhand about all this, that was little to the young man's fancy. It looked like a snare, and yet who could suppose a snare in such a quiet by-street and in a house of so prosperous and even noble an exterior? And yet—snare or no snare, intentionally or unintentionally—here he was, prettily trapped; and for the life of him he could see no way out of it again. The darkness began to weigh upon him. He gave ear; all was silent without, but within and close by he seemed to catch a faint sighing, a faint sobbing rustle, a little stealthy creak—as though many persons were at his side, holding themselves quite still, and governing even their respiration with the extreme of slyness. The idea went to his vitals with a shock, and he faced about suddenly as if to defend his life. Then, for the first time, he became aware of a light about the level of his eyes and at some distance in the interior of the house—a vertical thread of light, widening towards the bottom, such as might escape between two wings of arras over a doorway. To see anything was a relief to Denis; it was like a piece of solid ground to a man laboring in a morass; his mind seized upon it with avidity; and he stood staring at it and trying to piece together some logical conception of his surroundings. Plainly there was a flight of steps ascending from his own level to that of this illuminated doorway; and indeed he thought he could make out another thread of light, as fine as a needle and as faint as phosphorescence, which might very well be reflected along the polished wood of a handrail. Since he had begun to suspect that he was not alone, his heart had continued to beat with smothering violence, and an intolerable desire for action of any sort had possessed itself of his spirit. He was in deadly peril, he believed. What could be more natural than to mount the staircase, lift the curtain, and confront his difficulty at once? At least he would be dealing with something tangible; at least he would be no longer in the dark. He stepped slowly forward with outstretched hands, until his foot struck the bottom step; then he rapidly scaled the stairs, stood for a moment to compose his expression, lifted the arras and went in.

He found himself in a large apartment of polished stone. There were three doors; one on each of three sides; all similarly curtained with tapestry. The fourth side was occupied by two large windows and a great stone chimney-piece, carved with the arms of the Malétroits. Denis recognized the bearings, and was gratified to find himself in such good hands. The room was strongly illuminated; but it contained little furniture except a heavy table and a chair or two, the hearth was innocent of fire, and the pavement was but sparsely strewn with rushes clearly many days old.

On a high chair beside the chimney, and directly facing Denis as he entered, sat a little old gentleman in a fur tippet. He sat with his legs crossed and his hands folded, and a cup of spiced wine stood by his elbow on a bracket on the wall. His countenance had a strongly masculine cast; not properly human, but such as we see in the bull, the goat, or the domestic boar; something equivocal and wheedling, something greedy, brutal, and dangerous. The upper lip was inordinately full, as though swollen by a blow or a toothache; and the smile, the peaked eyebrows, and the small, strong eyes were quaintly and almost comically evil in expression. Beautiful white hair hung straight all round his head, like a saint's, and fell in a single curl upon the tippet. His beard and moustache were the pink of venerable sweetness. Age, probably in consequence of inordinate precautions, had left no mark upon his hands; and the Malétroit hand was famous. It would be difficult to imagine anything at once so fleshy and so delicate in design; the tapered, sensual fingers were like those of one of Leonardo's women; the fork of the thumb made a dimpled protuberance when closed; the nails were perfectly shaped, and of a dead, surprising whiteness. It rendered his aspect tenfold more redoubtable, that a man with hands like these should keep them devoutly folded like a virgin martyr— that a man with so intent and startling an expression of face should sit patiently on his seat and contemplate people with an unwinking stare, like a god, or a god's statue. His quiescence seemed ironical and treacherous, it fitted so poorly with his looks.

Such was Alain, Sire de Malétroit.

Denis and he looked silently at each other for a second or two.

"Pray step in," said the Sire de Malétroit. "I have been expecting you all the evening."

He had not risen but he accompanied his words with a smile and a slight but courteous inclination of the head. Partly from the smile, partly from the strange musical murmur with which the Sire prefaced his observation, Denis felt a strong shudder of disgust go through his marrow. And what with disgust and honest confusion of mind, he could scarcely get words together in reply.

"I fear," he said, "that this is a double accident. I am not the person you suppose me. It seems you were looking for a visit; but for my part, nothing was further from my thoughts—nothing could be more contrary to my wishes—than this intrusion."

"Well, well," replied the old gentleman indulgently, "here you are, which is the main point. Seat yourself, my friend, and put yourself entirely at your ease. We shall arrange our little affairs presently."

Denis perceived that the matter was still complicated with some misconception, and he hastened to continue his explanations.

"Your door . . . ." he began.

"About my door?" asked the other raising his peaked eyebrows. "A little piece of ingenuity." And he shrugged his shoulders. "A hospitable fancy! By your own account, you were not desirous of making my acquaintance. We old people look for such reluctance now and then; when it touches our honor, we cast about until we find some way of overcoming it. You arrive uninvited, but believe me, very welcome."

"You persist in error, sir," said Denis. "There can be no question between you and me. I am a stranger in this country-side. My name is Denis, damoiseau de Beaulieu. If you see me in your house, it is only——"

"My young friend," interrupted the other, "you will permit me to have my own ideas on that subject. They probably differ from yours at the present moment," he added with a leer, "but time will show which of us is in the right."

Denis was convinced he had to do with a lunatic. He seated himself with a shrug, content to wait the upshot; and a pause ensued, during which he thought he could distinguish a hurried gabbling as of prayer from behind the arras immediately opposite him. Sometimes there seemed to be but one person engaged, sometimes two; and the vehemence of the voice, low as it was, seemed to indicate either great haste or an agony of spirit. It occurred to him that this piece of tapestry covered the entrance to the chapel he had noticed from without.

The old gentleman meanwhile surveyed Denis from head to foot with a smile, and from time to time emitted little noises like a bird or a mouse, which seemed to indicate a high degree of satisfaction. This state of matters became rapidly insupportable; and Denis, to put an end to it, remarked politely that the wind had gone down.

The old gentleman fell into a fit of silent laughter, so prolonged and violent that he became quite red in the face. Denis got upon his feet at once, and put on his hat with a flourish.

"Sir," he said, "if you are in your wits, you have affronted me grossly. If you are out of them, I flatter myself I can find better employment for my brains than to talk with lunatics. My conscience is clear; you have made a fool of me from the first moment; you have refused to hear my explanations; and now there is no power under God will make me stay here any longer; and if I cannot make my way out in a more decent fashion, I will hack your door in pieces with my sword."

The Sire de Malétroit raised his right hand and wagged it at Denis with the fore and little fingers extended.

"My dear nephew," he said, "sit down."

"Nephew!" retorted Denis, "you lie in your throat;" and he snapped his fingers in his face.

"Sit down, you rogue!" cried the old gentleman, in a sudden, harsh voice, like the barking of a dog. "Do you fancy," he went on, "that when I had made my little contrivance for the door I had stopped short with that? If you prefer to be bound hand

and foot till your bones ache, rise and try to go away. If you
choose to remain a free young buck, agreeably conversing with
an old gentleman—why, sit where you are in peace, and God be
with you."

"Do you mean I am a prisoner?" demanded Denis.

"I state the facts," replied the other. "I would rather leave the
conclusion to yourself."

Denis sat down again. Externally he managed to keep pretty
calm, but within, he was now boiling with anger, now chilled
with apprehension. He no longer felt convinced that he was
dealing with a madman. And if the old gentleman was sane,
what, in God's name, had he to look for? What absurd or tragical adventure had befallen him? What countenance was he to
assume?

While he was thus unpleasantly reflecting, the arras that overhung the chapel door was raised, and a tall priest in his robes
came forth and, giving a long, keen stare at Denis, said something in an undertone to Sire de Malétroit.

"She is in a better frame of spirit?" asked the latter.

"She is more resigned, messire," replied the priest.

"Now the Lord help her, she is hard to please!" sneered the
old gentleman. "A likely stripling—not ill-born—and of her own
choosing, too? Why, what more would the jade have?"

"The situation is not usual for a young damsel," said the
other, "and somewhat trying to her blushes."

"She should have thought of that before she began the dance.
It was none of my choosing, God knows that; but since she is in
it, by our lady, she shall carry it to the end." And then address-
ing Denis, "Monsieur de Beaulieu," he asked, "may I present
you to my niece? She has been waiting your arrival, I may say,
with even greater impatience than myself."

Denis had resigned himself with a good grace—all he desired
was to know the worst of it as speedily as possible; so he rose at
once, and bowed in acquiescence. The Sire de Malétroit
followed his example and limped, with the assistance of the
chaplain's arm, towards the chapel-door. The priest pulled aside
the arras, and all three entered. The building had considerable
architectural pretensions. A light groining sprang from six stout

columns, and hung down in two rich pendants from the centre of the vault. The place terminated behind the altar in a round end, embossed and honeycombed with a superfluity of ornament in relief, and pierced by many little windows shaped like stars, trefoils, or wheels. These windows were imperfectly glazed, so that the night air circulated freely in the chapel. The tapers, of which there must have been half a hundred burning on the altar, were unmercifully blown about; and the light went through many different phases of brilliancy and semi-eclipse. On the steps in front of the altar knelt a young girl richly attired as a bride. A chill settled over Denis as he observed her costume; he fought with desperate energy against the conclusion that was being thrust upon his mind; it could not—it should not—be as he feared.

"Blanche," said the Sire, in his most flute-like tones, "I have brought a friend to see you, my little girl; turn round and give him your pretty hand. It is good to be devout; but it is necessary to be polite, my niece."

The girl rose to her feet and turned toward the new comers. She moved all of a piece; and shame and exhaustion were expressed in every line of her fresh young body; and she held her head down and kept her eyes upon the pavement, as she came slowly forward. In the course of her advance, her eyes fell upon Denis de Beaulieu's feet—feet of which he was justly vain, be it remarked, and wore in the most elegant accoutrement even while traveling. She paused—started, as if his yellow boots had conveyed some shocking meaning—and glanced suddenly up into the wearer's countenance. Their eyes met; shame gave place to horror and terror in her looks; the blood left her lips; with a piercing scream she covered her face with her hands and sank upon the chapel floor.

"That is not the man!" she cried. "My uncle, that is not the man!"

The Sire de Malétroit chirped agreeably. "Of course not," he said, "I expected as much. It was so unfortunate you could not remember his name."

"Indeed," she cried, "indeed, I have never seen this person till this moment—I have never so much as set eyes upon him—I never wish to see him again. Sir," she said, turning to Denis, "if you are a gentleman, you will bear me out. Have I ever seen you—have you ever seen me—before this accursed hour?"

"To speak for myself, I have never had that pleasure," answered the young man. "This is the first time, messire, that I have met with your engaging niece."

The old gentleman shrugged his shoulders.

"I am distressed to hear it," he said. "But it is never too late to begin. I had little more acquaintance with my own late lady ere I married her; which proves," he added, with a grimace, "that these impromptu marriages may often produce an excellent understanding in the long run. As the bridegroom is to have a voice in the matter, I will give him two hours to make up for lost time before we proceed with the ceremony." And he turned toward the door, followed by the clergyman.

The girl was on her feet in a moment. "My uncle, you cannot be in earnest," she said. "I declare before God I will stab myself rather than be forced on that young man. The heart rises at it; God forbids such marriages; you dishonor your white hair. Oh, my uncle, pity me! There is not a woman in all the world but would prefer death to such a nuptial. Is it possible," she added, faltering—"is it possible that you do not believe me—that you still think this"—and she pointed at Denis with a tremor of anger and contempt—"that you still think *this* to be the man?"

"Frankly," said the old gentleman, pausing on the threshold, "I do. But let me explain to you once for all, Blanche de Malétroit, my way of thinking about this affair. When you took it into your head to dishonor my family and the name that I have borne, in peace and war, for more than three-score years, you forfeited, not only the right to question my designs, but that of looking me in the face. If your father had been alive, he would have spat on you and turned you out of doors. His was the hand of iron. You may bless your God you have only to deal with the hand of velvet, mademoiselle. It was my duty to get you married without delay. Out of pure good-will, I have tried to find your own gallant for you. And I believe I have succeeded. But before God and all the holy angels, Blanche de Malétroit, if I have not, I care not one jack-straw. So let me recommend you to be polite to our young friend; for upon my word, your next groom may be less appetizing."

And with that he went out, with the chaplain at his heels; and the arras fell behind the pair.

The girl turned upon Denis with flashing eyes.

"And what, sir," she demanded, "may be the meaning of all this?"

"God knows," returned Denis, gloomily. "I am a prisoner in this house, which seems full of mad people. More I know not; and nothing do I understand."

"And pray how came you here?" she asked.

He told her as briefly as he could. "For the rest," he added, "perhaps you will follow my example, and tell me the answer to all these riddles, and what, in God's name, is like to be the end of it."

She stood silent for a little, and he could see her lips tremble and her tearless eyes burn with a feverish lustre. Then she pressed her forehead in both hands.

"Alas, how my head aches!" she said wearily—"to say nothing of my poor heart! But it is due to you to know my story, unmaidenly as it must seem. I am called Blanche de Malétroit; I have been without father or mother for—oh! for as long as I can recollect, and indeed I have been most unhappy all my life. Three months ago a young captain began to stand near me every day in church. I could see that I pleased him; I am much to blame, but I was so glad that anyone should love me; and when he passed me a letter, I took it home with me and read it with great pleasure. Since that time he has written many. He was so anxious to speak with me, poor fellow! and kept asking me to leave the door open some evening that we might have two words upon the stair. For he knew how much my uncle trusted me." She gave something like a sob at that, and it was a moment before she could go on. "My uncle is a hard man, but he is very shrewd," she said at last. "He has performed many feats in war, and was a great person at court, and much trusted by Queen Isabeau in old days. How he came to suspect me I cannot tell; but it is hard to keep anything from his knowledge; and this morning, as we came from mass, he took my hand into his, forced it open, and read my little billet, walking by my side all the while. When he finished, he gave it back to me with great politeness. It contained another request to have the door left open; and this has been the ruin of us all. My uncle kept me strictly in my room until evening, and then ordered me to dress myself as you see me—a hard mockery for a young girl, do you not think so? I suppose, when he could not prevail with me to tell him the young captain's name, he must have laid a trap for him: into which, alas! you have fallen in the anger of God. I looked for much confusion; for how could I tell whether he was willing to take me for his wife on these sharp terms? He might have been trifling with me from the first; or I might have made myself too cheap in his eyes. But truly I had not looked for such a shameful punishment as this! I could not think that God would let a girl be so disgraced before a young man. And now I tell you all; and I can scarcely hope that you will not despise me."

Denis made her a respectful inclination.

"Madam," he said, "you have honored me by your confidence. It remains for me to prove that I am not unworthy of the honor. Is Messire de Malétroit at hand?"

"I believe he is writing in the salle without," she answered.

"May I lead you thither, madam?" asked Denis, offering his hand with his most courtly bearing.

She accepted it; and the pair passed out of the chapel, Blanche in a very drooping and shamefast condition, but Denis strutting and ruffling in the consciousness of a mission, and the boyish certainty of accomplishing it with honor.

The Sire de Malétroit rose to meet them with an ironical obeisance.

"Sir," said Denis, with the grandest possible air, "I believe I am to have some say in the matter of this marriage; and let me tell you at once, I will be no party to forcing the inclination of this young lady. Had it been freely offered to me, I should have been proud to accept her hand, for I perceive she is as good as she is beautiful; but as things are, I have now the honor, messire, of refusing."

Blanche looked at him with gratitude in her eyes; but the old gentleman only smiled and smiled, until his smile grew positively sickening to Denis.

"I am afraid," he said, "Monsieur de Beaulieu, that you do not perfectly understand the choice I have offered you. Follow me, I beseech you, to this window." And he led the way to one of the large windows which stood open on the night. "You observe," he went on, "there is an iron ring in the upper masonry, and reeved through that, a very efficacious rope. Now, mark my words: if you should find your disinclination to my niece's person insurmountable, I shall have you hanged out of this window before sunrise. I shall only proceed to such an extremity with the greatest regret, you may believe me. For it is not at all your death that I desire, but my niece's establishment in life. At the same time, it must come to that if you prove obstinate. Your family, Monsieur de Beaulieu, is very well in its way; but if you sprang from Charlemagne, you should not refuse the hand of a Malétroit with impunity—not if she had been as common as the Paris road—not if she were as hideous as the gargoyle over my door. Neither my niece nor you, nor my own private feelings, move me at all in this matter. The honor of my house has been compromised; I believe you to be the guilty person, at least you are now in the secret; and you can hardly wonder if I request you to wipe out the stain. If you will not, your blood be on your own head! It will be no great satisfaction to me to have your interesting relics kicking their heels in the breeze below my windows, but half a loaf is better than no bread, and if I cannot cure the dishonor, I shall at least stop the scandal."

There was a pause.

"I believe there are other ways of settling such imbroglios among gentlemen," said Denis. "You wear a sword, and I hear you have used it with distinction."

The Sire de Malétroit made a signal to the chaplain, who crossed the room with long silent strides and raised the arras over the third of the three doors. It was only a moment before he let it fall again; but Denis had time to see a dusky passage full of armed men.

"When I was a little younger, I should have been delighted to honor you, Monsieur de Beaulieu," said Sire Alain; "but I am now too old. Faithful retainers are the sinews of age, and I must employ the strength I have. This is one of the hardest things to swallow as a man grows up in years; but with a little patience, even this becomes habitual. You and the lady seem to prefer the salle for what remains of your two hours; and as I have no desire to cross your preference, I shall resign it to your use with all the pleasure in the world. No haste!" he added, holding up his hand, as he saw a dangerous look come into Denis de Beaulieu's face. "If your mind revolt against hanging, it will be time enough two hours hence to throw yourself out of the window or upon the pikes of my retainers. Two hours of life are always two hours. A great many things may turn up in even as little a while as that. And, besides, if I understand her appearance, my niece has something to say to you. You will not disfigure your last hours by a want of politeness to a lady?"

Denis looked at Blanche, and she made him an imploring gesture.

It is likely that the old gentleman was hugely pleased at this symptom of an understanding; for he smiled on both, and added sweetly: "If you will give me your word of honor, Monsieur de Beaulieu, to await my return at the end of the two hours before attempting anything desperate, I shall withdraw my retainers, and let you speak in greater privacy with mademoiselle."

Denis again glanced at the girl, who seemed to beseech him to agree.

"I give you my word of honor," he said.

Messire de Malétroit bowed, and proceeded to limp about the apartment, clearing his throat the while with that odd musical chirp which had already grown so irritating in the ears of Denis de Beaulieu. He first possessed himself of some papers which lay upon the table; then he went to the mouth of the passage and appeared to give an order to the men behind the arras; and lastly he hobbled out through the door by which Denis had come in, turning upon the threshold to address a last smiling bow to the young couple, and followed by the chaplain with a hand-lamp.

No sooner were they alone than Blanche advanced towards Denis with her hands extended. Her face was flushed and excited, and her eyes shone with tears.

"You shall not die!" she cried, "you shall marry me after all."

"You seem to think, madam," replied Denis, "that I stand much in fear of death."

"Oh, no, no," she said, "I see you are no poltroon. It is for my own sake—I could not bear to have you slain for such a scruple."

"I am afraid," returned Denis, "that you underrate the difficulty, madam. What you may be too generous to refuse, I may be too proud to accept. In a moment of noble feeling towards me, you forgot what you perhaps owe to others."

He had the decency to keep his eyes on the floor as he said this, and after he had finished, so as not to spy upon her confusion. She stood silent for a moment, then walked suddenly away, and falling on her uncle's chair, fairly burst out sobbing. Denis was in the acme of embarrassment. He looked around, as if to seek for inspiration, and seeing a stool, plumped down upon it for something to do. There he sat playing with the guard of his rapier, and wishing himself dead a thousand times over, and buried in the nastiest kitchen-heap in France. His eyes wandered round the apartment, but found nothing to arrest them. There were such wide spaces between the furniture, the light fell so badly and cheerlessly over all, the dark outside air looked in so coldly through the windows, that he thought he had never seen a church so vast, nor a tomb so melancholy. The regular sobs of Blanche de Malétroit measured out the time like the ticking of a clock. He read the device upon the shield over and over again, until his eyes became obscured; he stared into shadowy corners until he imagined they were swarming with horrible animals; and every now and again he awoke with a start, to remember that his last two hours were running, and death was on the march.

Oftener and oftener, as the time went on, did his glance settle on the girl herself. Her face was bowed forward and covered with her hands, and she was shaken at intervals by the convulsive hiccup of grief. Even thus she was not an unpleasant object to dwell upon, so plump and yet so fine, with a warm brown skin, and the most beautiful hair, Denis thought, in the whole world of womankind. Her hands were like her uncle's; but they were more in place at the end of her young arms, and looked infinitely soft and caressing. He remembered how her blue eyes had shone upon him, full of anger, pity, and innocence. And the more he dwelt on her perfections, the uglier death looked, and the more deeply was he smitten with penitence at her continued tears. Now he felt that no man could have the courage to leave a world which contained so beautiful a creature; and now he would have given forty minutes of his last hour to have unsaid his cruel speech.

Suddenly a hoarse and ragged peal of cockcrow rose to their ears from the dark valley below the windows. And this shattering noise in the silence of all around was like a light in a dark place, and shook them both out of their reflections.

"Alas, can I do nothing to help you?" she said, looking up.

"Madam," replied Denis, with a fine irrelevancy, "if I have said anything to wound you, believe me, it was for your own sake and not for mine."

She thanked him with a tearful look.

"I feel your position cruelly," he went on. "The world has been bitter hard on you. Your uncle is a disgrace to mankind. Believe me, madam, there is no young gentleman in all France but would be glad of my opportunity, to die in doing you a momentary service."

"I know already that you can be very brave and generous," she answered. "What I *want* to know is whether I can serve you —now or afterwards," she added, with a quaver.

"Most certainly," he answered with a smile. "Let me sit beside you as if I were a friend, instead of a foolish intruder; try to forget how awkwardly we are placed to one another; make my last moments go pleasantly; and you will do me the chief service possible."

"You are very gallant," she added, with a yet deeper sadness . . . . "very gallant . . . . and it somehow pains me. But draw nearer, if you please; and if you find anything to say to me, you will at least make certain of a very friendly listener. Ah! Monsieur de Beaulieu," she broke forth—"ah! Monsieur de Beaulieu, how can I look you in the face?" And she fell to weeping again with a renewed effusion.

"Madam," said Denis, taking her hand in both of his, "reflect

on the little time I have before me, and the great bitterness into
which I am cast by the sight of your distress. Spare me, in my
last moments, the spectacle of what I cannot cure even with the
sacrifice of my life."

"I am very selfish," answered Blanche. "I will be braver, Monsieur de Beaulieu, for your sake. But think if I can do you no
kindness in the future—if you have no friends to whom I could
carry your adieux. Charge me as heavily as you can; every burden will lighten, by so little, the invaluable gratitude I owe you.
Put it in my power to do something more for you than weep."

"Mother is married again, and has a young family to care
for. My brother Guichard will inherit my fiefs; and if I am not
in error, that will content him amply for my death. Life is a little vapor that passeth away, as we are told by those in holy orders. When a man is in a fair way and sees all life open in front
of him, he seems to himself to make a very important figure in
the world. His horse whinnies to him; the trumpets blow and
the girls look out of the window as he rides into town before his
company; he receives many assurances of trust and regard—
sometimes by express in a letter—sometimes face to face, with
persons of great consequence falling on his neck. It is not wonderful if his head is turned for a time. But once he is dead, were
he as brave as Hercules or as wise as Solomon, he is soon forgotten. It is not ten years since my father fell, with many other
knights around him, in a very fierce encounter, and I do not
think that any one of them, nor so much as the name of the
fight, is now remembered. No, no, madam, the nearer you come
to it, you see that death is a dark and dusty corner, where a man
gets into his tomb and has the door shut after him till the judgment day. I have few friends just now, and once I am dead I shall
have none."

"Ah, Monsieur de Beaulieu!" she exclaimed, "you forget
Blanche de Malétroit."

"You have a sweet nature, madam, and you are pleased to es-
timate a little service far beyond its worth."

"It is not that," she answered. "You mistake me if you think
I am easily touched by my own concerns. I say so, because you
are the noblest man I have ever met; because I recognize in you

a spirit that would have made even a common person famous in the land."

"And yet here I die in a mousetrap—with no more noise about it than my own squeaking," answered he.

A look of pain crossed her face, and she was silent for a little while. Then a light came into her eyes, and with a smile she spoke again.

"I cannot have my champion think meanly of himself. Anyone who gives his life for another will be met in Paradise by all the heralds and angels of the Lord God. And you have no such cause to hang your head. For . . . . Pray, do you think me beautiful?" she asked, with a deep flush.

"Indeed, madam, I do," he said.

"I am glad of that," she answered heartily. "Do you think there are many men in France who have been asked in marriage by a beautiful maiden—with her own lips—and who have refused her to her face? I know you men would half despise such a triumph; but believe me, we women know more of what is precious in love. There is nothing that should set a person higher in his own esteem; and we women would prize nothing more dearly."

"You are very good," he said; "but you cannot make me forget that I was asked in pity and not for love."

"I am not so sure of that," she replied, holding down her head. "Hear me to an end, Monsieur de Beaulieu. I know how you must despise me; I feel you are right to do so; I am too poor a creature to occupy one thought of your mind, although, alas! you must die for me this morning. But when I asked you to marry me, indeed, and indeed, it was because I respected and admired you, and loved you with my whole soul, from the very moment that you took my part against my uncle. If you had seen yourself, and how noble you looked, you would pity rather than despise me. And now," she went on, hurriedly checking him with her hand, "although I have laid aside all reserve and told you so much, remember that I know your sentiments towards me already. I would not, believe me, being nobly born, weary you with importunities into consent. I too have a pride of my own: and I declare before the holy mother of God, if you should now go back from your word already given, I would no more marry you than I would marry my uncle's groom."

Denis smiled a little bitterly.

"It is a small love," he said, "that shies at a little pride."

She made no answer, although she probably had her own thoughts.

"Come hither to the window," he said with a sigh. "Here is the dawn."

And indeed the dawn was already beginning. The hollow of the sky was full of essential daylight, colorless and clean; and the valley underneath was flooded with a gray reflection. A few thin vapors clung in the coves of the forest or lay along the winding course of the river. The scene disengaged a surprising effect of stillness, which was hardly interrupted when the cocks began once more to crow among the steadings. Perhaps the same fellow who had made so horrid a clangor in the darkness not half an hour before, now sent up the merriest cheer to greet the coming day. A little wind went bustling and eddying among the tree-tops underneath the windows. And still the daylight kept flooding insensibly out of the east, which was soon to grow incandescent and cast up that red-hot cannon-ball, the rising sun.

Denis looked out over all this with a bit of a shiver. He had taken her hand, and retained it in his almost unconsciously.

"Has the day begun already?" she said; and then, illogically enough: "the night has been so long! Alas! what shall we say to my uncle when he returns?"

"What you will," said Denis, and he pressed her fingers in his.

She was silent.

"Blanche," he said, with a swift, uncertain, passionate utterance, "you have seen whether I fear death. You must know well enough that I would as gladly leap out of that window into the empty air as to lay a finger on you without your free and full consent. But if you care for me at all, do not let me lose my life in a misapprehension; for I love you better than the whole world; and though I will die for you blithely, it would be like all the joys of Paradise to live on and spend my life in your service."

As he stopped speaking, a bell began to ring loudly in the interior of the house; and a clatter of armor in the corridor showed that the retainers were returning to their post, and the two hours were at an end.

"After all that you have heard?" she whispered, leaning towards him with her lips and eyes.

"I have heard nothing," he replied.

"The captain's name was Florimond de Champdivers," she said in his ear.

"I did not hear it," he answered, taking her supple body in his arms, and covering her wet face with kisses.

A melodious chirping was audible behind, followed by a beautiful chuckle, and the voice of Messire de Malétroit wished his new nephew a good morning.

"Sire de Malétroit's Door"

Eric LaGuardia

One of the most striking qualities of this Stevenson story is its rhythm; there is a continuous and repetitious movement from the safe to the dangerous, the dangerous to the safe. Denis de Beaulieu is at first confident and happy; his life becomes endangered; he retreats to safety; he finds himself in danger again; and again he attempts to escape, only to involve himself in more danger. Finally, he is relieved of all threats, and the reader is released from the tensions of this rhythmic narrative. Denis' final union with Blanche is, in a way, less significant for the reader than the tension between safety and danger which preceded that union. It is the apprehension for and with Denis, the anticipation of his ultimate well-being rather than that well-being itself, which has the greatest effect on the reader. The form of the story, as Kenneth Burke would say, arouses and fulfills desires, but with the important qualification that the movement toward the union of Denis and Blanche is constantly turned aside by a series of threats and dangers. In fact, it is only these flights into danger and retreats to safety that make the ending possible at all; the pleasure of Denis' union with Blanche results from the painful circumstances which precede it. Pain here is a forerunner of pleasure.

In addition to this tension between safety and danger, the story has a striking quality of unreality. Together with the setting, which is remote in time, the preliminary description of the nocturnal experience gives the story an air of mystery and foreboding. There are, too, highly exaggerated characters: the derring-do, the cavalier, the chivalrous bearing of young Denis; the evil, threatening manner of Malétroit; and the absolute beauty and purity of Blanche. And, finally, the incredible nature of the tale itself, especially the devices of mistaken identity and coincidence, gives the reader the impression he has been introduced into a dream or phantasy world.

This impression is strengthened by the form of the story itself. Not only does the distortion of reality in the tale suggest that Stevenson has created a phantasy world; but, similarly, the insistence on danger as a preliminary of safety, or pain as a forerunner of pleasure, suggests that the phantasy is latently erotic. The erotic content is, of course, concealed beneath what the story manifestly pretends to be—a tale of romantic adventure, culminating in a union of hero and heroine. The danger-safety pattern, leading finally to the release of the tensions built up through the story, is a form common to the general category of adventure tales. An examination of the symbology of this Stevenson story reveals that the experience of the young hero is one of sexual attainment ultimately realized, but preceded by a number of painful elements which reflect the fear of such an attainment. The tension of the story, in other words, is between the desire for and fear of sexual fulfillment. Its erotic content, however, is transformed into an acceptable and apparently innocent tale of adventure and romance. We might suggest that in other phantastic stories of this type there may be discovered a latent erotic phantasy.

If we are going to consider the story as an erotic phantasy it will be necessary to think of Denis de Beaulieu as a young man in a position to demonstrate his manhood, but who is constantly faced with scenes of danger, threats and humiliations which hinder him, until the end, from the attainment of the sexual goal. That the hero is unaware of this goal as such, or even of the fact that Blanche resides in the Malétroit household, ought not to trouble us. The transformation of a sexual phantasy into a tale of romantic adventure (accomplished without doubt by Stevenson unconsciously) makes it necessary that the central figure be, so to speak, unaware of the real nature of his experiences. The central technique of mistaken identity gives the story, on its manifest level, an air of strangeness and terror. But on its latent level, the idea of mistaken identity leading to a romantic union is quite consistent with Denis' ambivalent fear of but desire for sexual attainment. We should be prepared to read the story, at every point, as an unconscious revelation of Denis' constantly painful flight forward toward the fulfillment of his manhood.

The problem at the moment is to understand the relevance of the danger-safety tension to Denis' erotic journey. Some of Theodor Reik's observations on what he calls the masochistic instinct, in his book *Masochism and Modern Man* (New York, 1941), provide, I think, some helpful clues for understanding Denis' problem and the erotic phantasy in which he is involved. One of the most important factors of the masochistic instinct is "attributable to the doubt or the hesitation as to whether or not an orgasm should be obtained. The desire to trespass the forbidden threshold is urgent enough, but the fear of the consequences is just as strong . . ." (p. 64). Thus, there is a tension which forces this kind of personality both to approach and recoil from sexual fulfillment. This tension, or this anxiety which is rooted in the fear of sexual attainment, is transformed into a pleasurable feeling. That is, "an anxiety-ridden pleasure slowly has developed into pleasurable anxiety" (p. 67). Thus the suspense which has been set up between the end-pleasure and the fear of reaching that pleasure is a source of satisfaction for the masochistic personality. The pleasure which he finds in discomfort serves to relieve his sexual anxieties. The suspense is, Reik observes, a "vacillation between the attempt to approach the pleasurable and the rejection of this temptation out of fear. A vacillation between the urge to approach and the urge to run away" (p. 118).

We see, then, that this pattern of sexual psychology involves the transformation of pain, scolding, and humiliation into pleasures so that the dread of sexual fulfillment may be relieved. Another important factor, and one related to suspense, which Reik has uncovered is that of anticipation. The primary goal in those phantasies which this kind of personality constructs, and which reveal his central preoccupation, is the pleasure of sexual attainment, not painful humiliation. Painful experiences are seen as pleasures only to relieve the dread of the flight forward to intercourse. The discomfort, in other words, is a necessary prelude to the prospective sexual pleasure. Pain "is only the herald, announcing the approach of the master, pleasure" (p. 135). Anticipation of this pleasure governs the phantasy constructions of the masochist; and it is an anticipation filled with an exciting dread and discomfort, so that the greater the humiliation experienced the greater the pleasure anticipated.

We can see, in "The Sire de Malétroit's Door," that the danger-safety pattern, the suspense between pain and well-being, may be taken as a verbal formula for the suspense between the desire to pass over the "forbidden threshold" of sex, and the fear of the consequences. There is, we may say, a latent suggestion in Denis' experiences that he is suffering from doubt or hesitation "as to whether or not an orgasm should be obtained." A vacillation "between the urge to approach and the urge to run away" is certainly evident throughout the story. The dangers, that is, bring Denis closer and closer to the point where he must demonstrate his manhood. The moments of safety, on the other hand, reflect his retreat from this task. Denis' curious penchant for painful situations implies that his doubts about his manhood (together with his overriding desire to fulfill it) lead him into a world of threats and humiliations, the suffering of which is a necessary prelude to his goal of sexual pleasure. We conclude, then, that "The Sire de Malétroit's Door," beneath its manifest intentions as a story of romantic adventure, has characteristics of an erotic phantasy which takes the form of what Reik has called "masochistic suspense." Not only is the vacillation between a flight forward toward sexual attainment and a withdrawal from that end-pleasure a significant feature of this story; there is the related (and equally significant) element of Denis' strange ability to get himself into threatening situations, indicating the intimate correspondence between discomfort and sexual attainment.

It is appropriate now to look at the story more closely. To facilitate an examination of the tale from the perspective outlined above, I have divided the phantasy into three main sections, *First*: the preliminary description of a phantasy world of safety and well-being; the subsequent introduction of a danger; and the temporary retreat to safety again. In this section we learn a good deal about Denis' character, we observe his night visit to his friend's house, we see his life threatened by a round of troops, and we accompany him in his retreat to safety behind Sire de Malétroit's door. *Second*: the double repetition of the danger-safety pattern; the meeting with Blanche, the sexual object; and the crucial humiliation and threat imposed by the Sire. In this section Denis loses his feeling of safeness again, and charges up the staircase to confront whatever the danger may be, only to discover a brightly lit apartment with the coat of arms of a noble family on the wall. This sense of well-being is short-lived as he learns more of his position, is introduced to Blanche, and suffers the discomfort of the old Sire's threat. *Third*: the agonies of indecision, and the final gratification of desire. In this last section, Denis torments himself with the alternatives of death and love; and the discomfort of the threat of death renders the final embrace with Blanche overwhelmingly ecstatic for him. We can see that the death threat represents the ultimate discomfort and thus logically precedes the lovers' orgastic embrace.

Section I—*The preliminary description of a phantasy world of safety and well-being; the subsequent introduction of a danger; and the temporary retreat to safety again.* We learn at the outset that Denis is twenty-one, but "he counted himself a grown man, and a very accomplished cavalier . . ." We also discover that "lads were early formed in that . . . epoch," that one becomes manly through "pitched battle," and that we should excuse Denis' swagger. These details concerning manliness and the test of manliness, together with the fact that Denis merely *thought* himself a man and therefore swaggered, are the first indications that he may have a conflict within himself—a conflict between wanting to be manly and the inability to be.

As Denis sets out on his visit in the "gray of the evening," he is in an "agreeable frame of mind." His entry into the night, however, "was not a very wise proceeding . . . the town was full of . . . troops"; and "though Denis was there on safe-conduct, his safe-conduct was like to serve him little on a chance encounter."

The phantasy world of Denis' adventures is at first peaceful and pleasant, but it also holds a potential of danger. The setting of this world is eerie and forbidding. It is windy and rainy, leaves are flying along the streets. The sounds of merry-making are "swallowed up and carried away by the wind." The sky is a "tumultuous, leaden chaos." The scene increases in tension as the pleasure he gained from his visit with his friend jars with the black and deathly quality of the night. His pleasant visit has been transformed into a terrifying and confusing journey through the ominous and enveloping darkness of the phantasy world. It is a world in which he is lost and must find his way; a world which is strange and discomforting. Denis' desire for manhood, or sexual fulfillment, is countered by feelings of terror and doubt; and therefore the nocturnal scene becomes figured with symbols of his central preoccupation—sexual attainment. He was not acquainted with "the intricate lanes" of the town, he knew he must keep "mounting the hill" for his inn was "up at the head, under the great church spire." For Denis it is "an eerie and mysterious position to be thus submerged in opaque blackness in an almost unknown town. The silence is terrifying in its possibilities." He now enters a narrow lane and comes upon the house in which he is about to have his most significant phantasy adventures, and it is represented with a wealth of phallic symbolism. It has pinnacles and turret-tops, the round stern of a chapel, flying buttresses, gargoyles, tapers within the chapel, a peaked roof. And, as he gazes at this house, it reminds him of his own; he compares its inhabitants to his own family.

The danger makes itself evident now in the form of a round of troops. Denis attracts their attention and, faced with the task of asserting himself against these soldiers, retreats to the door of the house, which opens and engulfs him in safety. This strange experience suggests that Denis has unconsciously sought a danger in order that he may escape it, and in this way prolong the moment when he must face the task before him. It is this pattern that is repeated throughout the story.

Denis becomes aware that the inner surface of this "black interior" behind the door is "quite smooth, not a handle, not a moulding, not a projection of any sort." The symbolic characteristics of a womb are obvious here, and justifiable if we conceive of Denis retreating to the safety of pre-birth, to a place where he cannot be called on to demonstrate his manhood. He draws his sword (another phallic symbol) immediately before being engulfed by the womb; no doubt a last moment and ineffectual exertion of his maleness. As he stands safely behind the door he hears the round of troops still searching for him, and a lance (still another phallic symbol) rattles on the door demanding, so to speak, that Denis come out and "be a man."

Thus far in his dream Denis has exhibited his strong preoccupation with the problem of attaining sexual gratification. The suspense of the narrative corresponds to the latent psychological tension between the desire for and fear of sex. His "flight forward" toward ultimate sexual pleasure is hindered by the appearance of danger, and later by mental humiliation and threats.

Section II—*The double repetition of the danger-safety pattern; the meeting with Blanche, the sexual object; and the crucial humiliation and threat imposed by Malétroit.* Denis senses a certain danger now in his position, but he is not yet able to accept the feeling: "It looked like a snare, and yet who could suppose a snare in such a quiet by-street and in a house of so prosperous and even noble exterior? And yet—snare or no snare, intentionally or unintentionally—here he was, prettily trapped; and for the life of him he could see no way out of it again." This threat suddenly becomes more concrete for him and "the idea went to his vitals with a shock." He whirls around "as if to defend his life." Safety is again transformed into a danger. The comfort of the womb denies the latent object of his journey—sexual expression. It is necessary, therefore, that he remove himself from this womb and face the danger that he has sensed. The means of exit from the womb is described in the most vivid symbolism, again, of sexual intercourse—indicative of his ultimate goal. He becomes aware of a flight of stairs and a shining handrail ascending to "a vertical thread of light, widening towards the bottom . . . What could be more natural than to mount the staircase, lift the curtain, and confront his difficulty at once?"

Through this erotic image Denis may be seen as taking an

additional "flight forward" toward ultimate pleasure. His ex-
citation by the promise of danger, however, falters immediately.
He returns to a state of timid well-being as he reacts to the fa-
miliarity of the apartment, and is gratified to discover the coat
of arms of a noble family. Slowly, though, an uncomfortable situation begins to build. The sight of Malétroit fills him with disgust. This old man is, for Denis, an ambiguous figure. His face
is strongly masculine, and there is a suggestion of greed and
brutality and danger about him. He has the white hair of a
saint, venerable sweetness; and, to climax the impression he
makes, his hands are sensuous and folded in his lap like a virgin martyr's. The fact that Denis associates this house with his
own, and that he felt in "good hands," or at home, suggests that
the figure of Sire de Malétroit is a latent image of his own
father; and the ambivalence of Denis' reaction indicates that
he both fears and admires him.

He is somehow wary of the possibilities of this confrontation,
and informs Malétroit: ". . . nothing could be more contrary to
my wishes—than this intrusion." The old man is not put off by
this and calmly tells Denis that their "little affairs" will be arranged presently, adding: "By your own account, you were not
desirous of making my acquaintance. We old people look for
such reluctance now and then; when it touches our honor, we
cast about until we find some way of overcoming it." He is
sure the figure of Malétroit is a threat to him; he is convinced
the man is a lunatic, and feels he is being humiliated. He as-
serts himself and demands to be released, threatening to hack
the door to pieces with the phallic sword. The door now becomes a symbol of the authority of the father figure, a restric-
tion of Denis' quest for sexual fulfillment in his dream.

Hostility between the two becomes more evident as Malétroit
refers to Denis as his "dear nephew" (a latent indication of
their blood relationship), and Denis replies: "you lie in your
throat." The old man is incensed at this remark, and with a
sudden, harsh voice informs Denis that he has a choice, a choice
which is symbolic of Denis' conflict between the desire for sexual success and the fear of it. If he surrenders to Malétroit's
humiliations he will remain "a free young buck"; but if he refuses he will be "bound hand and foot" until his "bones ache."

He chooses, of course, to remain a free young buck, for only in this way will he be able to attain his goal. To be bound hand and foot is to terminate his quest, to destroy his manhood, to castrate him. He is, nevertheless, a prisoner of the old Sire; and Denis no longer sees him as a madman. He is now boiling with anger and chilled with apprehension. The tension builds within him as the climax of the phantasy approaches, as he is about to be introduced to the object of his latent desire. Culmination is at hand, but how will he face it: "What countenance was he to assume?"

As Denis approaches his most significant experiences in the phantasy, it is understandable that his erotic goal should become more clearly defined. Thus, as the arras is pulled aside, the chapel in which he discovers Blanche is seen as a mass of symbols of male and female sexuality. "A light groining sprang from six stout columns, and hung down in two rich pendants from the centre of the vault. The place terminated behind the altar in a round end, embossed and honeycombed with a superfluity of ornament in relief, and pierced by many little windows shaped like stars, trefoils, or wheels. . . . The tapers, of which there must have been half a hundred burning on the altar, were unmercifully blown about; and the light went through many different phases of brilliancy and semi-eclipse." When Denis perceives that Blanche is dressed as a bride, a chill settles over him and he "fought with desperate energy against the conclusion that was being thrust upon his mind; it could not—it should not—be as he feared." His sexual incapabilities are reflected in this passage, and as Blanche rejects him as the wrong person they become even more evident. "Their eyes met; shame gave place to horror and terror in her looks; the blood left her lips; with a piercing scream she covered her face with her hands and sank upon the chapel floor."

Malétroit now explains to Denis that he expects him to marry Blanche. Denis attempts to extricate himself from this discomfort with a simple refusal, but the Sire makes it quite clear that he must choose between love and death. The final danger is upon him; he must either retreat from his sexuality or express it.

In this section of the story, the threat of the "father" is the most important element. On the manifest level of romantic adventure, the Sire is simply an old man who is in a position to make certain harsh demands upon Denis, whom he believes to be someone else. Consistent with our interpretation of the story as an erotic phantasy, however, the old Sire becomes an image of the threatening father, making uncomfortable demands on his son. The ambivalence of the father figure, explained in Freudian terms, is evident here. The Sire or the father does in fact urge Denis or the son on toward sexual attainment, but Denis sees this urging as a humiliation and a threat. Thus, the father functions as a figure who pushes the son on toward manhood, and threatens castration at the same time. The Sire controls Denis' destiny; he offers him at the same instant either the attainment or the destruction of his manhood.

Section III—*The agonies of indecision and the final gratification of desire.* After Malétroit leaves the chapel, the girl turns on Denis with flashing eyes. "And what, sir," she demands, "may be the meaning of all this?" "God knows," answers Denis, "I am a prisoner in this house, which seems full of mad people. More I know not; and nothing do I understand." "And pray how came you here?" she asks. And after telling her as briefly as he can, Denis adds, "For the rest perhaps you will follow my example, and tell me the answer to all these riddles, and what, in God's name, is like to be the end of it." Blanche gives him the details of the circumstance, and Denis, in a great show of honor to hide his fear, leads the girl back to Malétroit in the apartment without, and refuses to marry her, all the while insisting on her beauty and purity. Here again Denis is retreating from the humiliation of Malétroit because of his fear of the sexual act. His fear even leads him to challenge Malétroit to a duel; one manhood against the other, an attempt to destroy his father and relieve himself of the demands upon him. He relapses quickly, of course, into the depths of the needed humiliation as Malétroit makes even more vivid the dangers that await him. With a bow the old man leaves the young couple alone to decide whether to become married or not.

Blanche now exhibits an attraction and sympathy for Denis: "You shall not die!" she cries, "you shall marry me after all." She is asking to be taken, but Denis refuses: "I am afraid that you underrate the difficulty, madam. What you may be too generous to refuse, I may be too proud to accept." At these words Blanche bursts into tears, and Denis, thrown into acute discomfort, sits "playing with the guard of his rapier," examining his maleness, wondering what to do with it. They remain silent for a long interval, during which Denis takes notice of certain details in the apartment. "There were such wide spaces between furniture, the light fell so badly and cheerlessly over all . . . he had never seen a church so vast, nor a tomb so melancholy . . . he stared into shadowly corners until he imagined they were swarming with horrible animals; and every now and again he awoke with a start, to remember that his last two hours were running, and death was on the march."

These details of his fear and the danger he is in are in contrast with his reaction to Blanche. He begins to notice her more and more now, and she is, for him, "so plump and yet so fine, with a warm brown skin, and the most beautiful hair . . ." Her hands "looked infinitely caressing." The death alternative would certainly remove the task before him, but his desire for Blanche is increasing and about to replace the desire for death. However, he is still fearful of his acceptance by Blanche, still fearful that he is incapable of taking her. His long speech to her rationalizes his position; he insists the pleasures of the world are illusory, that no matter what one achieves in life, death will erase all success forever. Denis is attempting to justify his fears by denying the importance of manly accomplishments. "When a man is in a fair way and sees all life open in front of him, he seems to himself to make a very important figure in the world. His horse whinnies to him; the trumpets blow and the girls look out of the window as he rides into the town before his company; he receives many assurances of trust and regard —sometimes by express in a letter—sometimes face to face, with persons of great consequence falling on his neck. It is not wonderful if his head is turned for a time. But once he is dead, were he as brave as Hercules or as wise as Solomon, he is soon forgotten. . . . death is a dark and dusty corner, where a man gets into his tomb and has the door shut after him till the judgment day."

This passage is also remarkable as a kind of analog to Denis' personality conflict as it has been revealed so far in the story. Strangely enough, his surname can be translated as "in a fair way," and he does have all life open in front of him. We learned earlier that Denis swaggers, and this characteristic is echoed here as, "he seems to himself to make a very important figure in the world." His head is turned by the desire to express his manliness with Blanche, but he is about to get into his tomb and have the door shut after him.

Blanche now openly expresses her desire for him, but adds, ". . . if you should now go back from your word already given, I would no more marry you than I would marry my uncle's groom." Denis has got himself in a most uncomfortable situation, a situation in which the object of his instincts both wants and rejects him, in which he both wants and refuses her. Both the nature of his problem and the nature of the solution are indicated in this dilemma. The mutual attraction and rejection is, in terms of the erotic phantasy, a revelation of the "vacillation between the attempt to approach the pleasurable and the rejection of this temptation out of fear." And the resolution of this tension, which of course is imminent, seems to derive its pleasure from anticipating it from the perspective of agonizing discomfort. A pleasurable anticipation has arisen from a painful anxiety.

The predicament is resolved suddenly, almost irrationally, orgastically. "And still the daylight kept flooding insensibly out of the east, which was soon to grow incandescent and cast up that red-hot cannon-ball, the rising sun." "With a swift, uncertain, passionate utterance," Denis says, "Blanche, you have seen whether I fear death. You must know well enough that I would as gladly leap out of that window into the empty air as to lay a finger on you without your free and full consent." And in the final, orgastic moment of the phantasy Denis takes "her supple body in his arms," and covers "her wet face with kisses."

The erotic nature of this story is further attested by the coincidence between certain particulars of Denis' problem and the translations of the names of some of the characters. We have already noticed the occurrence of the English equivalent of Denis' surname. He is "in a fair way," he is at the stage when his self, his maleness demands to be expressed. The name of Denis' "rival," or more appropriately his "other self," Florimond de Champdivers, can be translated as "a flourishing, worldly man of many opportunities or careers." It is this kind of successful personality that Denis desires, and thus the story reveals that Denis de Beaulieu is a substitute for Florimond de Champdivers. Sire, of course, means lord or master; and one of the many possible translations for Malétroit is "evilly strict." As a father figure for Denis, the old man clearly exercises mastery over Denis; a mastery that is for him both evil and strict.

This examination of the symbology of "The Sire de Malétroit's Door" reveals that the story may be interpreted as an erotic phantasy. Once its surface intentions as a tale of romantic adventure have been pierced, it becomes evident that the situations, the characters, and the settings dramatize the tension between sexual desire and sexual fear, and resolve this tension in a physical union of the lovers. The construction of such a phantasy was most certainly done unconsciously by Stevenson. There is no reason to assume or insist that the author was aware of the sexual nature of his symbology. Freud's revelation of the obscure yet startling correspondence between sexual preoccupations and the manifest contents of dream and phantasy ought to be sufficient to convince us that one need not consciously try to establish connections between the erotic and the seemingly innocent. Indeed, it is one of Freud's major premises that the surface level of dream or phantasy exists simply to obscure the disturbing latent content. The application of this principle to literature, of course, is not always satisfactory. We would not claim, for example, that the discovery of erotic content in a piece of literature which seems quite innocent necessarily amounts to a total explanation of the work's significance or meaning. However, works such as "The Sire de Malétroit's Door"—that is, stories which are unreal and romantic—are often susceptible to probes beneath their literal level, and may reveal their more authentic content to be erotic. In addition, this kind of analysis need not be totally psychological. Certain issues, for example, concerning literary form have been touched on here. It may be possible to conclude, with evidence from other stories (by Stevenson or other writers), that the standard formal tension in adventures and romances between danger and well-being is a verbal formula for a psychological state of erotic suspense. The literary technique of creating and relieving tension may be seen as a formal counterpart to an erotic "vacillation between the attempt to approach the pleasurable and the rejection of this temptation out of fear."

COMMENT

Much of the work which has been done on Stevenson tends to imply that he was so emotionally repressed as to be totally unaware of the psychosexual content of his story, with the subsequent implication that such lack of control over the material severely qualifies the artistic stature of the piece. This essay has pointed to that peculiar and interesting function of language which *seems* to deal with an innocent, adventurous, or romantic world, but which can be shown to be under the surface charged with the frankest kind of sexual meaning. Many medieval romances and allegories operate the same way, but we need not go so far afield from contemporary popular culture to apply the method of the essay. It works well and interestingly for an analysis of many fairy tales or children's stories ("Peter Pan" for instance), comic strips (especially of the genre that comprises Superman, Captain Marvel, Plasticman), and typical adventure motion pictures (westerns, cops-and-robbers).

On the other hand, the subject of sexual repression is not uncommon in modern short stories, although here frequently the author's awareness of the nature of repression makes it part of the intention of the story, if not actually the major theme. One might examine in this light such stories as Elizabeth Bowen's "The Cat Jumps," Peter Taylor's "Spinster's Tale," and D. H. Lawrence's "The Horse-Dealer's Daughter."

IV

A Worn Path

Eudora Welty

It was December—a bright frozen day in the early morning. Far out in the country there was an old Negro woman with her head tied in a red rag, coming along a path through the pine-woods. Her name was Phoenix Jackson. She was very old and small and she walked slowly in the dark pine shadows, moving a little from side to side in her steps, with the balanced heaviness and lightness of a pendulum in a grandfather clock. She carried a thin, small cane made from an umbrella, and with this she kept tapping the frozen earth in front of her. This made a grave and persistent noise in the still air, that seemed meditative like the chirping of a solitary little bird.

She wore a dark striped dress reaching down to her shoe tops, and an equally long apron of bleached sugar sacks, with a full pocket: all neat and tidy, but every time she took a step she might have fallen over her shoelaces, which dragged from her unlaced shoes. She looked straight ahead. Her eyes were blue with age. Her skin had a pattern all its own of numberless branching wrinkles and as though a whole little tree stood in the middle of her forehead, but a golden color ran underneath, and the two knobs of her cheeks were illumined by a yellow burning under the dark. Under the red rag her hair came down on her neck in the frailest of ringlets, still black, and with an odor like copper.

Now and then there was a quivering in the thicket. Old Phoenix said, "Out of my way, all you foxes, owls, beetles, jack rabbits, coons and wild animals! . . . Keep out from under these feet, little bob-whites. . . . Keep the big wild hogs out of my path. Don't let none of those come running my direction. I got a long way." Under her small black-freckled hand her cane, limber as a buggy whip, would switch at the brush as if to rouse up any hiding things.

On she went. The woods were deep and still. The sun made the pine needles almost too bright to look at, up where the wind rocked. The cones dropped as light as feathers. Down in the hollow was the mourning dove—it was not too late for him.

The path ran up a hill. "Seem like there is chains about my feet, time I get this far," she said, in the voice of argument old people keep to use with themselves. "Something always take a hold of me on this hill—pleads I should stay."

After she got to the top she turned and gave a full, severe look behind her where she had come. "Up through pines," she said at length. "Now down through oaks."

Her eyes opened their widest, and she started down gently. But before she got to the bottom of the hill a bush caught her dress.

Her fingers were busy and intent, but her skirts were full and long, so that before she could pull them free in one place they were caught in another. It was not possible to allow the dress to tear. "I in the thorny bush," she said. "Thorns, you doing your appointed work. Never want to let folks pass, no sir. Old eyes thought you was a pretty little *green* bush."

Finally, trembling all over, she stood free, and after a moment dared to stoop for her cane.

"Sun so high!" she cried, leaning back and looking, while the thick tears went over her eyes. "The time getting all gone here."

At the foot of this hill was a place where a log was laid across the creek.

"Now comes the trial," said Phoenix.

Putting her right foot out, she mounted the log and shut her eyes. Lifting her skirt, leveling her cane fiercely before her, like a festival figure in some parade, she began to march across. Then she opened her eyes and she was safe on the other side.

"I wasn't as old as I thought," she said.

But she sat down to rest. She spread her skirts on the bank around her and folded her hands over her knees. Up above her was a tree in a pearly cloud of mistletoe. She did not dare to close her eyes, and when a little boy brought her a plate with a slice of marble-cake on it she spoke to him. "That would be acceptable," she said. But when she went to take it there was just her own hand in the air.

So she left that tree, and had to go through a barbed-wire fence. There she had to creep and crawl, spreading her knees and stretching her fingers like a baby trying to climb the steps. But she talked loudly to herself: she could not let her dress be torn now, so late in the day, and she could not pay for having her arm or her leg sawed off if she got caught fast where she was.

At last she was safe through the fence and risen up out in the clearing. Big dead trees, like black men with one arm, were standing in the purple stalks of the withered cotton field. There sat a buzzard.

"Who you watching?"

In the furrow she made her way along.

"Glad this not the season for bulls," she said, looking sideways, "and the good Lord made his snakes to curl up and sleep in the winter. A pleasure I don't see no two-headed snake coming around that tree, where it come once. It took a while to get by him, back in the summer."

She passed through the old cotton and went into a field of dead corn. It whispered and shook and was taller than her head. "Through the maze now," she said, for there was no path.

Then there was something tall, black, and skinny there, moving before her.

At first she took it for a man. It could have been a man dancing in the field. But she stood still and listened, and it did not make a sound. It was as silent as a ghost.

"Ghost," she said sharply, "who be you the ghost of? For I have heard of nary death close by."

But there was no answer—only the ragged dancing in the wind.

She shut her eyes, reached out her hand, and touched a sleeve. She found a coat and inside that an emptiness, cold as ice.

"You scarecrow," she said. Her face lighted. "I ought to be shut up for good," she said with laughter. "My senses is gone.

I too old. I the oldest people I ever know. Dance, old scarecrow," she said, "while I dancing with you."

She kicked her foot over the furrow, and with mouth drawn down, shook her head once or twice in a little strutting way. Some husks blew down and whirled in streamers about her skirts.

Then she went on, parting her way from side to side with the cane, through the whispering field. At last she came to the end, to a wagon track where the silver grass blew between the red ruts. The quail were walking around like pullets, seeming all dainty and unseen.

"Walk pretty," she said. "This the easy place. This the easy going."

She followed the track, swaying through the quiet bare fields, through the little strings of trees silver in their dead leaves, past cabins silver from weather, with the doors and windows boarded shut, all like old women under a spell sitting there. "I walking in their sleep," she said, nodding her head vigorously.

In a ravine she went where a spring was silently flowing through a hollow log. Old Phoenix bent and drank. "Sweet-gum makes the water sweet," she said, and drank more. "Nobody know who made this well, for it was here when I was born."

The track crossed a swampy part where the moss hung as white as lace from every limb. "Sleep on, alligators, and blow your bubbles." Then the track went into the road.

Deep, deep the road went down between the high green-colored banks. Overhead the live-oaks met, and it was as dark as a cave.

A black dog with a lolling tongue came up out of the weeds by the ditch. She was meditating, and not ready, and when he came at her she only hit him a little with her cane. Over she went in the ditch, like a little puff of milkweed.

Down there, her senses drifted away. A dream visited her, and she reached her hand up, but nothing reached down and gave her a pull. So she lay there and presently went to talking. "Old woman," she said to herself, "that black dog come up out of the weeds to stall you off, and now there he sitting on his fine tail, smiling at you."

A white man finally came along and found her—a hunter, a young man, with his dog on a chain.

"Well, Granny!" he laughed. "What are you doing there?"

"Lying on my back like a June-bug waiting to be turned over, mister," she said, reaching up her hand.

He lifted her up, gave her a swing in the air, and set her down. "Anything broken, Granny?"

"No sir, them old dead weeds is springy enough," said Phoenix, when she had got her breath. "I thank you for your trouble."

"Where do you live, Granny?" he asked, while the two dogs were growling at each other.

"Away back yonder, sir, behind the ridge. You can't even see it from here."

"On your way home?"

"No sir, I going to town."

"Why, that's too far! That's as far as I walk when I come out myself, and I get something for my trouble." He patted the stuffed bag he carried, and there hung down a little closed claw. It was one of the bob-whites, with its beak hooked bitterly to show it was dead. "Now you go on home, Granny!"

"I bound to go to town, mister," said Phoenix. "The time come around."

He gave another laugh, filling the whole landscape. "I know you old colored people! Wouldn't miss going to town to see Santa Claus!"

But something held old Phoenix very still. The deep lines in her face went into a fierce and different radiation. Without warning, she had seen with her own eyes a flashing nickel fall out of the man's pocket onto the ground.

"How old are you, Granny?" he was saying.

"There is no telling, mister," she said, "no telling."

Then she gave a little cry and clapped her hands and said, "Git on away from here, dog! Look! Look at that dog!" She laughed as if in admiration. "He ain't scared of nobody. He a big black dog." She whispered, "Sic him!"

"Watch me get rid of that cur," said the man. "Sic him, Pete! Sic him!"

Phoenix heard the dogs fighting, and heard the man running and throwing sticks. She even heard a gunshot. But she was slowly bending forward by that time, further and further forward, the lids stretched down over her eyes, as if she were doing this in her sleep. Her chin was lowered almost to her knees. The yellow palm of her hand came out from the fold of her apron. Her fingers slid down and along the ground under the piece of money with the grace and care they would have in lifting an egg from under a setting hen. Then she slowly straightened up, she stood erect, and the nickel was in her apron pocket. A bird flew by. Her lips moved. "God watching me the whole time. I come to stealing."

The man came back, and his own dog panted about them. "Well, I scared him off that time," he said, and then he laughed and lifted his gun and pointed it at Phoenix.

She stood straight and faced him.

"Doesn't the gun scare you?" he said, still pointing it.

"No, sir, I seen plenty go off closer by, in my day, and for less than what I done," she said, holding utterly still.

He smiled, and shouldered the gun. "Well, Granny," he said, "you must be a hundred years old, and scared of nothing. I'd give you a dime if I had any money with me. But you take my advice and stay home, and nothing will happen to you."

"I bound to go on my way, mister," said Phoenix. She inclined her head in the red rag. Then they went in different directions, but she could hear the gun shooting again and again over the hill.

She walked on. The shadows hung from the oak trees to the road like curtains. Then she smelled wood-smoke, and smelled the river, and she saw a steeple and the cabins on their steep steps. Dozens of little black children whirled around her. There ahead was Natchez shining. Bells were ringing. She walked on.

In the paved city it was Christmas time. There were red and green electric lights strung and criss-crossed everywhere, and all turned on in the daytime. Old Phoenix would have been lost if she had not distrusted her eyesight and depended on her feet to know where to take her.

She paused quietly on the sidewalk where people were pass-

ing by. A lady came along in the crowd, carrying an armful of
red-, green- and silver-wrapped presents; she gave off perfume
like the red roses in hot summer, and Phoenix stopped her.

"Please, missy, will you lace up my shoe?" She held up her
foot.

"What do you want, Grandma?"

"See my shoe," said Phoenix. "Do all right for out in the
country, but wouldn't look right to go in a big building."

"Stand still then, Grandma," said the lady. She put her packages down on the sidewalk beside her and laced and tied both
shoes tightly.

"Can't lace 'em with a cane," said Phoenix. "Thank you,
missy. I doesn't mind asking a nice lady to tie up my shoe, when
I gets out on the street."

Moving slowly and from side to side, she went into the big
building, and into a tower of steps, where she walked up and
around and around until her feet knew to stop.

She entered a door, and there she saw nailed up on the wall
the document that had been stamped with the gold seal and
framed in the gold frame, which matched the dream that was
hung up in her head.

"Here I be," she said. There was a fixed and ceremonial stiffness over her body.

"A charity case, I suppose," said an attendant who sat at the
desk before her.

But Phoenix only looked above her head. There was sweat
on her face, the wrinkles in her skin shone like a bright net.

"Speak up, Grandma," the woman said. "What's your name?
We must have your history, you know. Have you been here before? What seems to be the trouble with you?"

Old Phoenix only gave a twitch to her face as if a fly were
bothering her.

"Are you deaf?" cried the attendant.

But then the nurse came in.

"Oh, that's just old Aunt Phoenix," she said. "She doesn't
come for herself—she has a little grandson. She makes these trips
just as regular as clockwork. She lives away back off the Old
Natchez Trace." She bent down. "Well, Aunt Phoenix, why

don't you just take a seat? We won't keep you standing after your long trip." She pointed.

The old woman sat down, bolt upright in the chair.

"Now, how is the boy?" asked the nurse.

Old Phoenix did not speak.

"I said, how is the boy?"

But Phoenix only waited and stared straight ahead, her face very solemn and withdrawn into rigidity.

"Is his throat any better?" asked the nurse. "Aunt Phoenix, don't you hear me? Is your grandson's throat any better since the last time you came for the medicine?"

With her hands on her knees, the old woman waited, silent, erect and motionless, just as if she were in armor.

"You mustn't take up our time this way, Aunt Phoenix," the nurse said. "Tell us quickly about your grandson, and get it over. He isn't dead, is he?"

At last there came a flicker and then a flame of comprehension across her face, and she spoke.

"My grandson. It was my memory had left me. There I sat and forgot why I made my long trip."

"Forgot?" The nurse frowned. "After you came so far?"

Then Phoenix was like an old woman begging a dignified forgiveness for waking up frightened in the night. "I never did go to school, I was too old at the Surrender," she said in a soft voice. "I'm an old woman without an education. It was my memory fail me. My little grandson, he is just the same, and I forgot it in the coming."

"Throat never heals, does it?" said the nurse, speaking in a loud, sure voice to old Phoenix. By now she had a card with something written on it, a little list. "Yes. Swallowed lye. When was it?—January—two-three years ago—"

Phoenix spoke unasked now. "No, missy, he not dead, he just the same. Every little while his throat begin to close up again, and he not able to swallow. He not get his breath. He not able to help himself. So the time come around, and I go on another trip for the soothing medicine."

"All right. The doctor said as long as you came to get it, you could have it," said the nurse. "But it's an obstinate case."

"My little grandson, he sit up there in the house all wrapped up, waiting by himself," Phoenix went on. "We is the only two left in the world. He suffer and it don't seem to put him back at all. He got a sweet look. He going to last. He wear a little patch quilt and peep out holding his mouth open like a little bird. I remembers so plain now. I not going to forget him again, no, the whole enduring time. I could tell him from all the others in creation."

"All right." The nurse was trying to hush her now. She brought her a bottle of medicine. "Charity," she said, making a check mark in a book.

Old Phoenix held the bottle close to her eyes, and then carefully put it into her pocket.

"I thank you," she said.

"It's Christmas time, Grandma," said the attendant. "Could I give you a few pennies out of my purse?"

"Five pennies is a nickel," said Phoenix stiffly.

"Here's a nickel," said the attendant.

Phoenix rose carefully and held out her hand. She received the nickel and then fished the other nickel out of her pocket and laid it beside the new one. She stared at her palm closely, with her head on one side.

Then she gave a tap with her cane on the floor.

"This is what come to me to do," she said. "I going to the store and buy my child a little windmill they sells, made out of paper. He going to find it hard to believe there such a thing in the world. I'll march myself back where he waiting, holding it straight up in this hand."

She lifted her free hand, gave a little nod, turned around, and walked out of the doctor's office. Then her slow step began on the stairs, going down.

Life for Phoenix

NEIL D. ISAACS

The first four sentences of "A Worn Path" contain simple de-
clarative statements using the simple past of the verb to be: "It
was December . . . ," ". . . there was an old Negro woman . . . ,"
"Her name was Phoenix Jackson," "She was very old and
small . . ." The note of simplicity thus struck is the keynote of
Eudora Welty's artistic design in the story. For it is a simple
story (a common reaction is "simply beautiful"). But it is also
a story which employs many of the devices which can make of
the modern short story an intricate and densely complex form.
It uses them, however, in such a way that it demonstrates how
a single meaning may be enriched through the use of various
techniques. Thus, instead of various levels of meaning, we have
here a single meaning reinforced on several levels of perception. Moreover, there is no muddying of levels and techniques;
they are neatly arranged, straightforwardly presented, and simply perceived.

The plot-line follows Phoenix Jackson, who is graphically
described in the second paragraph, on her long walk into Natchez where she has to get medicine for her grandson. The trek
is especially difficult because of her age, and in the process of
struggling on she forgets the reason for the struggle. At the end
she has remembered, received the medicine, and decided to buy
the child a Christmas present with the ten cents she has acquired
during the day.

What makes this a story? It barely appears to fulfill even
Sidney Cox's generous criterion of "turning a corner or at least
a hair." But it does belong to a specific storyteller's genre familiar from Homer to Fielding to Kerouac—"road" literature. This

form provides a ready-made plot pattern with some inherent weaknesses. The story concerns the struggle to achieve a goal, the completion of the journey; and the story's beginning, middle, and end are the same as those of the road. The primary weakness of this structure is its susceptibility to too much middle.

A traditional concept of road literature, whether the mythical journey of the sun across the heavens or a boy's trip down the Mississippi or any other variation, is its implicit equation with life: the road of life, life's journey, ups and downs, the straight and narrow, and a host of other clichés reflect the universality of this primitive metaphor. "A Worn Path" makes explicit, beginning with the very title, Eudora Welty's acceptance of the traditional equation as a basic aspect of the story. In fact, the whole meaning of "A Worn Path" will rely on an immediate recognition of the equation—the worn path equals the path of life—which is probably why it is so explicit. But we needn't start with a concept which is metaphorical or perhaps primitively allegorical. It will probably be best for us to begin with the other literal elements in the story: they will lead us back to the sub- or supraliteral eventually anyway.

An important part of the setting is the time element, that is, the specific time of the year. We learn immediately that it is "a bright frozen day" in December, and there are several subsequent, direct statements which mark it more precisely as Christmas time. The hunter talks about Santa Claus and the attendant at the hospital says that "It's Christmas time," echoing what the author has said earlier. There are several other references and images forming a pattern to underline the idea of Christmas time, such as "Up above her was a tree in a pearly cloud of *mistletoe*."* Notice especially the elaborate color pattern of red, green, and silver, the traditional colors of Christmas. It begins with Phoenix's head "in a *red* rag, coming along a path through the *pinewoods*" (which are green as well as Christmas trees). Later, she sees "a wagon track where the *silver grass* blew between the *red* ruts" and "little strings of trees *silver* in their dead leaves" (reddish brown?). This pattern comes to a

---

* *Author's italics*—here and in other quoted passages from "The Worn Path."

climax in the description of the city and the lady's packages, which also serves to make explicit its purpose, return it to the literal: "There were red and green electric lights strung and crisscrossed everywhere . . ."; ". . . an armful of red-, green- and silver-wrapped presents."

From the plot-line alone the idea of Christmas doesn't seem to be more than incidental, but it is obvious from the persistent references that Christmas is going to play an important part in the total effect of the story. Besides the direct statements already mentioned, there proliferates around the pattern throughout the story a dense cluster of allusions to and suggestions of the Christmas myth at large and to the *meanings* of Christmas in particular. For instance, as Phoenix rests under a tree, she has a vision of a little boy offering her a slice of marble-cake on a little plate, and she says, "That would be acceptable." The allusion here is to Communion and Church ritual. Later, when a bird flies by, Phoenix says, "God watching me the whole time." Then there are references to the Eden story (the ordering of the species, the snake in summer to be avoided), to the parting of the Red Sea (Phoenix walking through the field of corn), to a sequence of temptations, to the River Jordan and the City of Heaven (when Phoenix gets to the river, sees the city shining, and hears the bells ringing; then there is the angel who waits on her, tying her shoes), to the Christ-child in the manger (Phoenix describing her grandson as "all wrapped up" in "a little patch quilt . . . like a little bird" with "a sweet look"). In addition, the whole story is suggestive of a religious pilgrimage, while the conclusion implies that the return trip will be like the journey of the Magi, with Phoenix following a star (the marvelous windmill) to bring a gift to the child (medicine, also windmill). Moreover, there's the hunter who is, in part, a Santa Claus figure himself (he carries a big sack over his shoulder, he is always laughing, he brings Phoenix a gift of a nickel).

The richness of all this evocation of a Christianity-Christmas frame of reference heightens the specific points about the meanings of Christmas. The Christmas spirit, of course, is the Christian ethic in its simplest terms: giving, doing for others, charity.

This concept is made explicit when the nurse says of Phoenix, "She doesn't come for herself." But it had already been presented in a brilliant piece of ironic juxtaposition:

> She entered a door, and there she saw *nailed up on the wall* the document that had been stamped with the *gold seal* and framed in the *gold frame,* which *matched the dream that was hung up in her head.*
> *"Here I be,"* she said. There was a *fixed and ceremonial stiffness* over her body.
> "A *charity* case, I suppose," said an attendant . . .

Amid the Christmas season and the dense Christmas imagery, Phoenix, with an abiding intuitive faith, arrives at the shrine of her pilgrimage, beholds a symbolic crucifixion, presents herself as a celebrant in the faith, and is recognized as an embodiment of the message of the faith. This entire scene, however, with its gold trimming and the attitude of the attendant, is turned ironically to suggest greed, corruption, cynicism—the very opposite of the word used, charity. Yet the episode, which is Phoenix's final and most severe trial, also results in her final emergence as a redeemer and might be called her calvary.

Perhaps a better way to get at the meaning of Christmas and the meaning of "A Worn Path" is to talk about life and death. In a sense, the meaning of Christmas and that of Easter are the same—a celebration of life out of death. (Notice that Phoenix refers to herself as a *June* bug and that the woman with the packages "gave off perfume like the *red roses in hot summer.*") Christ is born in the death of the year and in a near-dead nature-society situation in order to rejuvenate life itself, naturally and spiritually. He dies in order that the life of others may be saved. He is reborn out of death, and so are nature, love, and the spirit of man. All this is the potent Christian explanation of the central irony of human existence, that life means death and death is life. One might state the meaning of "A Worn Path" in similar terms, where Phoenix endures a long, agonizing dying in order to redeem her grandson's life. So the medicine, which the nurse calls charity as she makes a check in her book, is a symbol of love and life. The windmill represents the same duality, but lighter sides of both aspects. If the path is the path of life, then its end is death and the purpose of that death is new life.

It would be misleading, however, to suggest that the story is merely a paralleling of the Christian nature-myth. It is, rather, a miniature nature-myth of its own which uses elements of many traditions. The most obvious example is the name Phoenix from the mythological Egyptian bird, symbol of immortality and resurrection, which dies so that a new Phoenix may emerge from its ashes. There is a reference to the Daedalus labyrinth myth when Phoenix walks through the corn field and Miss Welty puns: " 'Through the maze now,' " she said, "for there was no path." That ambivalent figure of the hunter comes into play here as both a death figure (killer, bag full of slain quail) and a life figure (unconscious giver of life with the nickel, banisher of Cerberus-like black dog who is attacking Phoenix), but in any case a folk-legend figure who can fill "the whole landscape" with his laugh. And there are several references to the course of the sun across the sky which gives a new dimension to the life-road equation; e.g., "Sun so high! The time getting all gone here."

The most impressive extra-Christian elements are the patterns that identify Phoenix as a creature of nature herself and as a ritual-magic figure. Thus, Phoenix makes a sound "like the chirping of a solitary little bird," her hair has "an odor like copper," and at one point "with her mouth drawn down, [she] shook her head once or twice in a little strutting way." Even more remarkable is the "fixed and ceremonial stiffness" of her body, which moves "like a festival figure in some parade." The cane she carries, made from an umbrella, is tapped on the ground like a magic wand, and she uses it to "switch at the brush as if to rouse up any hiding things." At the same time she utters little spells: "Out of my way, all you foxes, owls, beetles, jack rabbits, coons, and wild animals! . . . Keep out from under these feet, little bob-whites. . . . Keep the big wild hogs out of my path. Don't let none of those come running my direction"; "Ghost, who be you the ghost of?"; "Sweet-gum makes the water sweet . . . Nobody knows who made this well, for it was here when I was born"; "Sleep on, alligators, and blow your bubbles." Other suggestions of magic appear in the whirling of

cornhusks in streamers about her skirts, when she parts "her way
from side to side with the cane, through the whispering field,"
when the quail seem "unseen," and when the cabins are "all
like old women under a spell sitting there." Finally, ironically,
when Phoenix swings at the black dog, she goes over "in the
ditch, like a little puff of milkweed."

More or less remote, more or less direct, all these allusions
are used for the same effect as the references to Christianity, to
reinforce a statement of the meaning of life. This brings us back
to the basic life-road equation of the story, and there are numerous indications that the path is life and that the end of the
road is death and renewal of life. These suggestions are of three
types; a few examples for each should suffice. First, there are
statements which relate the road, the trip, or Phoenix to time:
Phoenix walks "with the balanced heaviness and lightness of a
pendulum in a grandfather clock"; she tells the hunter, "I
bound to go . . . The time come around"; and the nurse says,
"She makes these trips just as regular as clockwork." Second
(the most frequent type), there are descriptions of the road or
episodes along the way which are suggestive of life, usually in
a simple metaphorical way: "I got a long way" (ambiguously
referring to past and future); "I in the thorny bush"; "Up
through pines . . . Now down through oaks"; "This the easy
place. This the easy going." Third, there are direct references
to death, age, and life: Phoenix says to a buzzard, "Who you
watching?" and to a scarecrow, "Who be you the ghost of? For
I have heard of nary death close by"; then she performs a little
dance of death with the scarecrow after she says, "My senses is
gone. I too old. I the oldest people I ever know."

This brings us full circle in an examination of the design of
the story, and it should be possible now to say something about
the total meaning of "A Worn Path." The path is the path of
life, and the story is an attempt to probe the meaning of life in
its simplest, most elementary terms. Through the story we arrive at a definition of life, albeit a teleological one. When the
hunter tells Phoenix to "take my advice and stay home, and
nothing will happen to you," the irony is obvious and so is the
metaphor: don't live and you can't die. When Phoenix forgets

why she has made the arduous trek to Natchez, we understand that it is only a rare person who knows the meaning of his life, that living does not imply knowing. When Phoenix describes the Christlike child waiting for her and says, "I not going to forget him again, no, the whole enduring time. I could tell him from all the others in creation," we understand several things about it: her life is almost over, she sees clearly the meaning of life, she has an abiding faith in that meaning, and she will share with her grandson this great revelation just as together they embody its significance. And when Phoenix's "slow step began on the stairs, going down," as she starts back to bring the boy the medicine and the windmill, we see a composite symbol of life itself, dying so that life may continue. Life is a journey toward death, because one must die in order that life may go on.

COMMENT

The scrutiny of the imagery and allusions of a short story, particularly where they fall into patterns, is an elementary approach. The reader using such an approach begins with positive evidence—the words themselves, with their denotative, connotative, and contextual meanings—and does not have to supply a framework for study from outside the story. It is recommended that the student try this approach for any story, to see whether common denominators among images cause them to fall into patterns. If the patterns become evident, they should support the meaning(s) of the story on their own level.

V

Ethan Brand

A Chapter from an Abortive Romance

NATHANIEL HAWTHORNE

Bartram the lime-burner, a rough, heavy-looking man, begrimed with charcoal, sat watching his kiln, at nightfall, while his little son played at building houses with the scattered fragments of marble, when, on the hillside below them, they heard a roar of laughter, not mirthful, but slow, and even solemn, like a wind shaking the boughs of the forest.

"Father, what is that?" asked the little boy, leaving his play, and pressing betwixt his father's knees.

"Oh, some drunken man, I suppose," answered the lime-burner; "some merry fellow from the bar-room in the village, who dared not laugh loud enough within doors lest he should blow the roof of the house off. So here he is, shaking his jolly sides at the foot of Graylock."

"But, father," said the child, more sensitive than the obtuse, middle-aged clown, "he does not laugh like a man that is glad. So the noise frightens me!"

"Don't be a fool, child!" cried his father, gruffly. "You will never make a man, I do believe; there is too much of your mother in you. I have known the rustling of a leaf startle you. Hark! Here comes the merry fellow now. You shall see that there is no harm in him."

Bartram and his little son, while they were talking thus, sat watching the same lime-kiln that had been the scene of Ethan Brand's solitary and meditative life, before he began his search for the Unpardonable Sin. Many years, as we have seen, had now elapsed, since that portentous night when the IDEA was first developed. The kiln, however, on the mountain-side, stood unimpaired, and was in nothing changed since he had thrown his dark thoughts into the intense glow of its furnace, and melted them, as it were, into the one thought that took possession of his life. It was a rude, round, tower-like structure about twenty feet high, heavily built of rough stones, and with a hillock of earth heaped about the larger part of its circumference; so that the blocks and fragments of marble might be drawn by cart-loads, and thrown in at the top. There was an opening at the bottom of the tower, like an oven-mouth, but large enough to admit a man in a stooping posture, and provided with a massive iron door. With the smoke and jets of flame issuing from the chinks and crevices of this door, which seemed to give admittance into the hillside, it resembled nothing so much as the private entrance to the infernal regions, which the shepherds of the Delectable Mountains were accustomed to show to pilgrims.

There are many such lime-kilns in that tract of country, for the purpose of burning the white marble which composes a large part of the substance of the hills. Some of them, built years ago, and long deserted, with weeds growing in the vacant round of the interior, which is open to the sky, and grass and wild-flowers rooting themselves into the chinks of the stones, look already like relics of antiquity, and may yet be overspread with the lichens of centuries to come. Others, where the lime-burner still feeds his daily and night-long fire, afford points of interest to the wanderer among the hills, who seats himself on a log of wood or a fragment of marble, to hold a chat with the solitary man. It is a lonesome, and, when the character is inclined to thought, may be an intensely thoughtful occupation; as it proved in the case of Ethan Brand, who had mused to such strange purpose, in days gone by, while the fire in this very kiln was burning.

The man who now watched the fire was of a different order, and troubled himself with no thoughts save the very few that were requisite to his business. At frequent intervals, he flung back the clashing weight of the iron door, and, turning his face from the insufferable glare, thrust in huge logs of oak, or stirred the immense brands with a long pole. Within the furnace were seen the curling and riotous flames, and the burning marble, almost molten with the intensity of heat; while without, the reflection of the fire quivered on the dark intricacy of the surrounding forest, and showed in the foreground a bright and ruddy little picture of the hut, the spring beside its door, the athletic and coal-begrimed figure of the lime-burner, and the half-frightened child, shrinking into the protection of his father's shadow. And when again the iron door was closed, then reappeared the tender light of the half-full moon, which vainly strove to trace out the indistinct shapes of the neighboring mountains; and, in the upper sky, there was a flitting congregation of clouds, still faintly tinged with the rosy sunset, though thus far down into the valley the sunshine had vanished long and long ago.

The little boy now crept still closer to his father, as footsteps were heard ascending the hillside, and a human form thrust aside the bushes that clustered beneath the trees.

"Halloo! who is it?" cried the lime-burner, vexed at his son's timidity, yet half infected by it. "Come forward, and show yourself, like a man, or I'll fling this chunk of marble at your head!"

"You offer me a rough welcome," said a gloomy voice, as the unknown man drew nigh. "Yet I neither claim nor desire a kinder one, even at my own fireside."

To obtain a distincter view, Bartram threw open the iron door of the kiln, whence immediately issued a gush of fierce light, that smote full upon the stranger's face and figure. To a careless eye there appeared nothing very remarkable in his aspect, which was that of a man in a coarse, brown, country-made suit of clothes, tall and thin, with the staff and heavy shoes of a wayfarer. As he advanced, he fixed his eyes—which were very bright—intently upon the brightness of the furnace, as if he beheld, or expected to behold, some object worthy of note within it.

"Good evening, stranger," said the lime-burner; "whence come you, so late in the day?"

"I come from my search," answered the wayfarer; "for, at last, it is finished."

"Drunk!—or crazy!" muttered Bartram to himself. "I shall have trouble with the fellow. The sooner I drive him away, the better."

The little boy, all in a tremble, whispered to his father, and begged him to shut the door of the kiln, so that there might not be so much light; for that there was something in the man's face which he was afraid to look at, yet could not look away from. And, indeed, even the lime-burner's dull and torpid sense began to be impressed by an indescribable something in that thin, rugged, thoughtful visage, with the grizzled hair hanging wildly about it, and those deeply sunken eyes, which gleamed like fires within the entrance of a mysterious cavern. But, as he closed the door, the stranger turned towards him, and spoke in a quiet, familiar way, that made Bartram feel as if he were a sane and sensible man, after all.

"Your task draws to an end, I see," said he. "This marble has already been burning three days. A few hours more will convert the stone to lime."

"Why, who are you?" exclaimed the lime-burner. "You seem as well acquainted with my business as I am myself."

"And well I may be," said the stranger; "for I followed the same craft many a long year, and here, too, on this very spot. But you are a new-comer in these parts. Did you never hear of Ethan Brand?"

"The man that went in search of the Unpardonable Sin?" asked Bartram, with a laugh.

"The same," answered the stranger. "He has found what he sought, and therefore he comes back again."

"What! then you are Ethan Brand himself?" cried the lime-burner, in amazement. "I am a new-comer here, as you say, and they call it eighteen years since you left the foot of Graylock. But, I can tell you, the good folks still talk about Ethan Brand, in the village yonder, and what a strange errand took him away from his lime-kiln. Well, and so you have found the Unpardonable Sin?"

"Even so!" said the stranger, calmly.

"If the question is a fair one," proceeded Bartram, "where might it be?"

Ethan Brand laid his finger on his own heart.

"Here!" replied he.

And then, without mirth in his countenance, but as if moved by an involuntary recognition of the infinite absurdity of seeking throughout the world for what was the closest of all things to himself, and looking into every heart, save his own, for what was hidden in no other breast, he broke into a laugh of scorn. It was the same slow, heavy laugh, that had almost appalled the lime-burner when it heralded the wayfarer's approach.

The solitary mountain-side was made dismal by it. Laughter, when out of place, mistimed, or bursting forth from a disordered state of feeling, may be the most terrible modulation of the human voice. The laughter of one asleep, even if it be a little child—the madman's laugh—the wild, screaming laugh of a born idiot—are sounds that we sometimes tremble to hear, and would willingly forget. Poets have imagined no utterance of fiends or hobgoblins so fearfully appropriate as a laugh. And even the obtuse lime-burner felt his nerves shaken, as this strange man looked inward at his own heart, and burst into laughter that rolled away into the night, and was indistinctly reverberated among the hills.

"Joe," said he to his little son, "scamper down to the tavern in the village, and tell the jolly fellows there that Ethan Brand has come back, and that he has found the Unpardonable Sin!"

The boy darted away on his errand, to which Ethan Brand made no objection, nor seemed hardly to notice it. He sat on a log of wood, looking steadfastly at the iron door of the kiln. When the child was out of sight, and his swift and light footsteps ceased to be heard treading first on the fallen leaves and then on the rocky mountain-path, the lime-burner began to regret his departure. He felt that the little fellow's presence had been a barrier between his guest and himself, and that he must now deal, heart to heart, with a man who, on his own confession, had committed the one only crime for which Heaven could afford no mercy. That crime, in its indistinct blackness, seemed to overshadow him. The lime-burner's own sins rose up within him, and made his memory riotous with a throng of evil shapes that asserted their kindred with the Master Sin, whatever it might be, which it was within the scope of man's corrupted nature to conceive and cherish. They were all of one family; they went to and fro between his breast and Ethan Brand's, and carried dark greetings from one to the other.

Then Bartram remembered the stories which had grown traditionary in reference to this strange man, who had come upon him like a shadow of the night, and was making himself at home in his old place, after so long absence that the dead people, dead and buried for years, would have had more right to be at home, in any familiar spot, than he. Ethan Brand, it was said, had conversed with Satan himself in the lurid blaze of this very kiln. The legend had been matter of mirth heretofore, but looked grisly now. According to this tale, before Ethan Brand departed on his search, he had been accustomed to evoke a fiend from the hot furnace of the lime-kiln, night after night, in order to confer with him about the Unpardonable Sin; the man and the fiend each laboring to frame the image of some mode of guilt which could neither be atoned for nor forgiven. And, with the first gleam of light upon the mountaintop, the fiend crept in at the iron door, there to abide the intensest element of fire, until again summoned forth to share in the dreadful task of extending man's possible guilt beyond the scope of Heaven's else infinite mercy.

While the lime-burner was struggling with the horror of these thoughts, Ethan Brand rose from the log, and flung open the door of the kiln. The action was in such accordance with the idea in Bartram's mind, that he almost expected to see the Evil One issue forth, red-hot, from the raging furnace.

"Hold! hold!" cried he, with a tremulous attempt to laugh; for he was ashamed of his fears, although they overmastered him. "Don't, for mercy's sake, bring out your Devil now!"

"Man!" sternly replied Ethan Brand, "what need have I of the Devil? I have left him behind me, on my track. It is with such half-way sinners as you that he busies himself. Fear not, because I open the door. I do but act by old custom, and am going to trim your fire, like a lime-burner, as I was once."

He stirred the vast coals, thrust in more wood, and bent forward to gaze into the hollow prison-house of the fire, regardless of the fierce glow that reddened upon his face. The lime-burner sat watching him, and half suspected this strange guest of a purpose, if not to evoke a fiend, at least to plunge bodily into the flames, and thus vanish from the sight of man. Ethan Brand, however, drew quietly back, and closed the door of the kiln.

"I have looked," said he, "into many a human heart that was seven times hotter with sinful passions than yonder furnace is with fire. But I found not there what I sought. No, not the Unpardonable Sin!"

"What is the Unpardonable Sin?" asked the lime-burner; and then he shrank farther from his companion, trembling lest his question should be answered.

"It is a sin that grew within my own breast," replied Ethan Brand, standing erect, with a pride that distinguishes all enthusiasts of his stamp. "A sin that grew nowhere else! The sin of an intellect that triumphed over the sense of brotherhood with man and reverence for God, and sacrificed everything to its own mighty claims! The only sin that deserves a recompense of immortal agony! Freely, were it to do again, would I incur the guilt. Unshrinkingly I accept the retribution!"

"The man's head is turned," muttered the lime-burner to himself. "He may be a sinner like the rest of us,—nothing more likely,—but, I'll be sworn, he is a madman too."

Nevertheless, he felt uncomfortable at his situation, alone with Ethan Brand on the wild mountain-side, and was right glad to hear the rough murmur of tongues, and the footsteps of what seemed a pretty numerous party, stumbling over the stones and rustling through the underbrush. Soon appeared the whole lazy regiment that was wont to infest the village tavern, comprehending three or four individuals who had drunk flip beside the bar-room fire through all the winters, and smoked their pipes beneath the stoop through all the summers, since Ethan Brand's departure. Laughing boisterously, and mingling all their voices together in unceremonious talk, they now burst into the moonshine and narrow streaks of firelight that illuminated the open space before the lime-kiln. Bartram set the door ajar again, flooding the spot with light, that the whole company might get a fair view of Ethan Brand, and he of them.

There, among other old acquaintances, was a once ubiquitous man, now almost extinct, but whom we were formerly sure to encounter at the hotel of every thriving village throughout the country. It was the stage-agent. The present specimen of the genus was a wilted and smoke-dried man, wrinkled and red-nosed, in a smartly cut, brown, bob-tailed coat, with brass buttons, who, for a length of time unknown, had kept his desk and corner in the bar-room, and was still puffing what seemed to be the same cigar that he had lighted twenty years before. He had great fame as a dry joker, though, perhaps, less on account of any intrinsic humor than from a certain flavor of brandy-toddy and tobacco-smoke, which impregnated all his ideas and expressions, as well as his person. Another well-remembered, though strangely altered, face was that of Lawyer Giles, as people still called him in courtesy; an elderly ragamuffin, in his soiled shirt-sleeves and tow-cloth trousers. This poor fellow had been an attorney, in what he called his better days, a sharp practitioner, and in great vogue among the village litigants; but flip, and sling, and toddy, and cocktails, imbibed at all hours, morning, noon, and night, had caused him to slide from intellectual to various kinds and degrees of bodily labor, till at last, to adopt his own phrase, he slid into a soap-vat. In other words, Giles was now a soap-boiler, in a small way. He had come to be but the fragment of a human being, a part of one foot having been chopped off by an axe, and an entire hand torn away by the devilish grip of a steam-engine. Yet, though the corporeal hand was gone, a spiritual member remained; for, stretching forth the stump, Giles steadfastly averred that he felt an invisible thumb and fingers with as vivid a sensation as before the real ones were amputated. A maimed and miserable wretch he was; but one, nevertheless, whom the world could not trample on, and had no right to scorn, either in this or any previous stage of his misfortunes, since he had still kept up the courage and spirit of a man, asked nothing in charity, and with his one hand—and that the left one—fought a stern battle against want and hostile circumstances.

Among the throng, too, came another personage, who, with certain points of similarity to Lawyer Giles, had many more of difference. It was the village doctor; a man of some fifty years, whom, at an earlier period of his life, we introduced as paying a professional visit to Ethan Brand during the latter's supposed insanity. He was now a purple-visaged, rude, and brutal, yet half-gentlemanly figure, with something wild, ruined, and desperate in his talk, and in all the details of his gesture and manners. Brandy possessed this man like an evil spirit, and made him as surly and savage as a wild beast, and as miserable as a lost soul; but there was supposed to be in him such wonderful skill, such native gifts of healing, beyond any which medical science could impart, that society caught hold of him, and would not let him sink out of its reach. So, swaying to and fro upon his horse, and grumbling thick accents at the bedside, he visited all the sick-chambers for miles about among the mountain towns, and sometimes raised a dying man, as it were, by miracle, or quite as often, no doubt, sent his patient to a grave that was dug many a year too soon. The doctor had an everlasting pipe in his mouth, and, as somebody said, in allusion to his habit of swearing, it was always alight with hell-fire.

These three worthies pressed forward, and greeted Ethan Brand each after his own fashion, earnestly inviting him to partake of the contents of a certain black bottle, in which, as they averred, he would find something far better worth seeking for than the Unpardonable Sin. No mind, which has wrought itself by intense and solitary meditation into a high state of enthusiasm, can endure the kind of contact with low and vulgar modes of thought and feeling to which Ethan Brand was now subjected. It made him doubt—and, strange to say, it was a painful doubt—whether he had indeed found the Unpardonable Sin, and found it within himself. The whole question on which he had exhausted life, and more than life, looked like a delusion.

"Leave me," he said bitterly, "ye brute beasts, that have made yourselves so, shrivelling up your souls with fiery liquors! I have done with you. Years and years ago, I groped into your hearts, and found nothing there for my purpose. Get ye gone!"

"Why, you uncivil scoundrel," cried the fierce doctor, "is that the way you respond to the kindness of your best friends? Then let me tell you the truth. You have no more found the Unpardonable Sin than yonder boy Joe has. You are but a crazy fellow,—I told you so twenty years ago,—neither better nor worse than a crazy fellow, and the fit companion of old Humphrey, here!"

He pointed to an old man, shabbily dressed, with long white

hair, thin visage, and unsteady eyes. For some years past this aged person had been wandering about among the hills, inquiring of all travellers whom he met for his daughter. The girl, it seemed, had gone off with a company of circus-performers; and occasionally tidings of her came to the village, and fine stories were told of her glittering appearance as she rode on horseback in the ring, or performed marvellous feats on the tight-rope.

The white-haired father now approached Ethan Brand, and gazed unsteadily into his face.

"They tell me you have been all over the earth," said he, wringing his hands with earnestness. "You must have seen my daughter, for she makes a grand figure in the world, and everybody goes to see her. Did she send any word to her old father, or say when she was coming back?"

Ethan Brand's eye quailed beneath the old man's. That daughter, from whom he so earnestly desired a word of greeting, was the Esther of our tale, the very girl whom, with such cold and remorseless purpose, Ethan Brand had made the subject of a psychological experiment, and wasted, absorbed, and perhaps annihilated her soul, in the process.

"Yes," murmured he, turning away from the hoary wanderer; "it is no delusion. There is an Unpardonable Sin!"

While these things were passing, a merry scene was going forward in the area of cheerful light, beside the spring and before the door of the hut. A number of the youth of the village, young men and girls, had hurried up the hillside, impelled by curiosity to see Ethan Brand, the hero of so many a legend familiar to their childhood. Finding nothing, however, very remarkable in his aspect,—nothing but a sunburnt wayfarer, in plain garb and dusty shoes, who sat looking into the fire as if he fancied pictures among the coals,—these young people speedily grew tired of observing him. As it happened, there was other amusement at hand. An old German Jew, travelling with a diorama on his back, was passing down the mountain-road towards the village just as the party turned aside from it, and, in hopes of eking out the profits of the day, the showman had kept them company to the lime-kiln.

"Come, old Dutchman," cried one of the young men, "let us see your pictures, if you can swear they are worth looking at!"

"Oh, yes, Captain," answered the Jew,—whether as a matter of courtesy or craft, he styled everybody Captain,—"I shall show you, indeed, some very superb pictures!"

So, placing his box in a proper position, he invited the young men and girls to look through the glass orifices of the machine, and proceeded to exhibit a series of the most outrageous scratchings and daubings, as specimens of the fine arts, that ever an itinerant showman had the face to impose upon his circle of spectators. The pictures were worn out, moreover, tattered, full of cracks and wrinkles, dingy with tobacco-smoke, and otherwise in a most pitiable condition. Some purported to be cities, public edifices, and ruined castles in Europe; others represented Napoleon's battles and Nelson's sea-fights; and in the midst of these would be seen a gigantic, brown, hairy hand,—which might have been mistaken for the Hand of Destiny, though, in truth, it was only the showman's,—pointing its forefinger to various scenes of the conflict, while its owner gave historical illustrations. When, with much merriment at its abominable deficiency of merit, the exhibition was concluded, the German bade little Joe put his head into the box. Viewed through the magnifying-glasses, the boy's round, rosy visage assumed the strangest imaginable aspect of an immense Titanic child, the mouth grinning broadly, and the eyes and every other feature overflowing with fun at the joke. Suddenly, however, that merry face turned pale, and its expression changed to horror, for this easily impressed and excitable child had become sensible that the eye of Ethan Brand was fixed upon him through the glass.

"You make the little man to be afraid, Captain," said the German Jew, turning up the dark and strong outline of his visage, from his stooping posture. "But look again, and, by chance, I shall cause you to see somewhat that is very fine, upon my word!"

Ethan Brand gazed into the box for an instant, and then starting back, looked fixedly at the German. What had he seen? Nothing, apparently; for a curious youth, who had peeped in almost at the same moment, beheld only a vacant space of canvas.

"I remember you now," muttered Ethan Brand to the showman.

"Ah, Captain," whispered the Jew of Nuremberg, with a dark smile, "I find it to be a heavy matter in my show-box,—this Unpardonable Sin! By my faith, Captain, it has wearied my shoulders, this long day, to carry it over the mountain."

"Peace," answered Ethan Brand, sternly, "or get thee into the furnace yonder!"

The Jew's exhibition had scarcely concluded, when a great, elderly dog—who seemed to be his own master, as no person in the company laid claim to him—saw fit to render himself the object of public notice. Hitherto, he had shown himself a very quiet, well-disposed old dog, going round from one to another, and, by way of being sociable, offering his rough head to be patted by any kindly hand that would take so much trouble. But now, all of a sudden, this grave and venerable quadruped, of his own mere motion, and without the slightest suggestion from anybody else, began to run round after his tail, which, to heighten the absurdity of the proceeding, was a great deal shorter than it should have been. Never was seen such headlong eagerness in pursuit of an object that could not possibly be attained; never was heard such a tremendous outbreak of growling, snarling, barking, and snapping,—as if one end of the ridiculous brute's body were at deadly and most unforgivable enmity with the other. Faster and faster, round about went the cur; and faster and still faster fled the unapproachable brevity of his tail; and louder and fiercer grew his yells of rage and animosity; until, utterly exhausted, and as far from the goal as ever, the foolish old dog ceased his performance as suddenly as he had begun it. The next moment he was as mild, quiet, sensible, and respectable in his deportment, as when he first scraped acquaintance with the company.

As may be supposed, the exhibition was greeted with universal laughter, clapping of hands, and shouts of encore, to which the canine performer responded by wagging all that there was to wag of his tail, but appeared totally unable to repeat his very successful effort to amuse the spectators.

Meanwhile, Ethan Brand had resumed his seat upon the log, and moved, it might be, by a perception of some remote analogy between his own case and that of this self-pursuing cur, he broke into the awful laugh, which, more than any other token, expressed the condition of his inward being. From that moment, the merriment of the party was at an end; they stood aghast, dreading lest the inauspicious sound should be reverberated around the horizon, and that mountain would thunder it to mountain, and so the horror be prolonged upon their ears. Then, whispering one to another that it was late,—that the moon was almost down,—that the August night was growing chill,—they hurried homewards, leaving the lime-burner and little Joe to deal as they might with their unwelcome guest. Save for these three human beings, the open space on the hillside was a solitude, set in a vast gloom of forest. Beyond that darksome verge, the firelight glimmered on the stately trunks and almost black foliage of pines, intermixed with the lighter verdure of sapling oaks, maples, and poplars, while here and there lay the gigantic corpses of dead trees, decaying on the leaf-strewn soil. And it seemed to little Joe—a timorous and imaginative child—that the silent forest was holding its breath until some fearful thing should happen.

Ethan Brand thrust more wood into the fire, and closed the door of the kiln; then looking over his shoulder at the lime-burner and his son, he bade, rather than advised, them to retire to rest.

"For myself, I cannot sleep," said he. "I have matters that it concerns me to meditate upon. I will watch the fire, as I used to do in the old time."

"And call the Devil out of the furnace to keep you company, I suppose," muttered Bartram, who had been making intimate acquaintance with the black bottle above mentioned. "But watch, if you like, and call as many devils as you like! For my part, I shall be all the better for a snooze. Come, Joe!"

As the boy followed his father into the hut, he looked back at the wayfarer, and the tears came into his eyes, for his tender spirit had an intuition of the bleak and terrible loneliness in which this man had enveloped himself.

When they had gone, Ethan Brand sat listening to the crackling of the kindled wood, and looking at the little spirits of fire that issued through the chinks of the door. These trifles, however, once so familiar, had but the slightest hold of his attention, while deep within his mind he was reviewing the gradual but marvellous change that had been wrought upon him by the search to which he had devoted himself. He remembered how the night dew had fallen upon him,—how the dark forest had whispered to him,—how the stars had gleamed upon him,—a simple and loving man, watching his fire in the years gone by, and ever musing as it burned. He remembered with what tenderness, with what love and sympathy for mankind, and what pity for human guilt and woe, he had first begun to contemplate those ideas which afterwards became the inspiration of his life; with what reverence he had then looked into the heart of man, viewing it as a temple originally divine, and, however desecrated, still to be held sacred by a brother; with what awful fear he had deprecated the success of his pursuit, and prayed that the Unpardonable Sin might never be revealed to him. Then ensued that vast intellectual development, which, in its progress, disturbed the counterpoise between his mind and heart. The Idea that possessed his life had operated as a means of education; it had gone on cultivating his powers to the highest point of which they were susceptible; it had raised him from the level of an unlettered laborer to stand on a starlit eminence, whither the philosophers of the earth, laden with the lore of universities, might vainly strive to clamber after him. So much for the intellect! But where was the heart? That, indeed, had withered,—had contracted,—had hardened,—had perished! It had ceased to partake of the universal throb. He had lost his hold of the magnetic chain of humanity. He was no longer a brother-man, opening the chambers or the dungeons of our common nature by the key of holy sympathy, which gave him a right to share in all its secrets; he was now a cold observer, looking on mankind as the subject of his experiment, and, at length, converting man and woman to be his puppets, and pulling the wires that moved them to such degrees of crime as were demanded for his study.

Thus Ethan Brand became a fiend. He began to be so from the moment that his moral nature had ceased to keep the pace of improvement with his intellect. And now, as his highest effort and inevitable development,—as the bright and gorgeous flower, and rich, delicious fruit of his life's labor,—he had produced the Unpardonable Sin!

"What more have I to seek? what more to achieve?" said Ethan Brand to himself. "My task is done, and well done!"

Starting from the log with a certain alacrity in his gait and ascending the hillock of earth that was raised against the stone circumference of the lime-kiln, he thus reached the top of the structure. It was a space of perhaps ten feet across, from edge to edge, presenting a view of the upper surface of the immense mass of broken marble with which the kiln was heaped. All these innumerable blocks and fragments of marble were red-hot and vividly on fire, sending up great spouts of blue flame, which quivered aloft and danced madly, as within a magic circle, and sank and rose again, with continual and multitudinous activity. As the lonely man bent forward over this terrible body of fire, the blasting heat smote up against his person with a breath that, it might be supposed, would have scorched and shrivelled him up in a moment.

Ethan Brand stood erect, and raised his arms on high. The blue flames played upon his face, and imparted the wild and ghastly light which alone could have suited its expression; it was that of a fiend on the verge of plunging into his gulf of intensest torment.

"O Mother Earth," cried he, "who art no more my Mother, and into whose bosom this frame shall never be resolved! O mankind, whose brotherhood I have cast off, and trampled thy great heart beneath my feet! O stars of heaven, that shone on me of old, as if to light me onward and upward!—farewell all, and forever. Come, deadly element of Fire,—henceforth my familiar frame! Embrace me, as I do thee!"

That night the sound of a fearful peal of laughter rolled

heavily through the sleep of the lime-burner and his little son; dim shapes of horror and anguish haunted their dreams, and seemed still present in the rude hovel, when they opened their eyes to the daylight.

"Up, boy, up!" cried the lime-burner, staring about him. "Thank Heaven, the night is gone, at last; and rather than pass such another, I would watch my lime-kiln, wide awake, for a twelvemonth. This Ethan Brand, with his humbug of an Unpardonable Sin, has done me no such mighty favor, in taking my place!"

He issued from the hut, followed by little Joe, who kept fast hold of his father's hand. The early sunshine was already pouring its gold upon the mountain-tops, and though the valleys were still in shadow, they smiled cheerfully in the promise of the bright day that was hastening onward. The village, completely shut in by hills, which swelled away gently about it, looked as if it had rested peacefully in the hollow of the great hand of Providence. Every dwelling was distinctly visible; the little spires of the two churches pointed upwards, and caught a foreglimmering of brightness from the sun-gilt skies upon their gilded weathercocks. The tavern was astir, and the figure of the old, smoke-dried stage-agent, cigar in mouth, was seen beneath the stoop. Old Graylock was glorified with a golden cloud upon his head. Scattered likewise over the breasts of the surrounding mountains, there were heaps of hoary mist, in fantastic shapes, some of them far down into the valley, others high up towards the summits, and still others, of the same family of mist or cloud, hovering in the gold radiance of the upper atmosphere. Stepping from one to another of the clouds that rested on the hills, and thence to the loftier brotherhood that sailed in air, it seemed almost as if a mortal man might thus ascend into the heavenly regions. Earth was so mingled with sky that it was a day-dream to look at it.

To supply that charm of the familiar and homely, which Nature so readily adopts into a scene like this, the stage coach was rattling down the mountain-road, and the driver sounded his horn, while Echo caught up the notes, and intertwined them into a rich and varied and elaborate harmony, of which the original performer could lay claim to little share. The great hills played a concert among themselves, each contributing a strain of airy sweetness.

Little Joe's face brightened at once.

"Dear father," cried he, skipping cheerily to and fro, "that strange man is gone, and the sky and the mountains all seem glad of it!"

"Yes," growled the lime-burner, with an oath, "but he has let the fire go down, and no thanks to him if five hundred bushels of lime are not spoiled. If I catch the fellow hereabouts again, I shall feel like tossing him into the furnace!"

With his long pole in his hand, he ascended to the top of the kiln. After a moment's pause, he called to his son.

"Come up here, Joe!" said he.

So little Joe ran up the hillock, and stood by his father's side. The marble was all burnt into perfect, snow-white lime. But on its surface, in the midst of the circle,—snow-white too, and thoroughly converted into lime,—lay a human skeleton, in the attitude of a person who, after long toil, lies down to long repose. Within the ribs—strange to say—was the shape of a human heart.

"Was the fellow's heart made of marble?" cried Bartram, in some perplexity at this phenomenon. "At any rate, it is burnt into what looks like special good lime; and, taking all the bones together, my kiln is half a bushel the richer for him."

So saying, the rude lime-burner lifted his pole, and, letting it fall upon the skeleton, the relics of Ethan Brand were crumbled into fragments.

Blake's Urizen as Hawthorne's Ethan Brand

GLENN PEDERSEN

One of the beauties of the art form is the infinite variety of expression it contains. Often a part of the aesthetic delight in art comes from the recognition of universal experience in a new expression; we have learned to recognize the same experience or idea expressed in the various media of art. We hear color in music and see rhythm in paint; we see motion in sculpture as in the dance. Less fleeting and ephemeral to define are those ideas expressed in the variations of the same medium such as the words of a poet and a novelist. A student begins to see the integrity of art as universal expression when he recognizes the same or nearly similar ideas in the works of artists creating independent of each other, but essentially dependent upon a more complete expression which all artists share.

Such a shared idea we find in Blake and Hawthorne. Ethan Brand, like other Hawthorne characters, creates a literal as well as artistic impact upon the reader; we keep the character beside us in the sphere of his action long after we lay the story aside; he has a significance that lives in his own defined limit and that we translate into our own experience. But how much further he extends as character and how much deeper he descends as experience when we see him as the mentally benighted character of William Blake's cosmic myth. Ethan Brand immediately becomes psychically personal and the reader simultaneously extends the former finity of his microcosm toward the complete integrity of universal art. The widened world the reader experiences as he identifies ideas common to the creators of art becomes an ever more enlightened sphere in which to experience further poetic expression.

Students of Blake become aware that in Blake's myth Satan is the extreme degradation of the mental act; he is Urizen (the mental Zoa) in the lowest state of fall. That the conscious mind, intent upon maintaining a superior position of judgment, is inimical to emotional expression is a commonplace, at least insofar as the mind interdicts its continuous "Thou shalt not" to emotional experience. In this role, Satan is the Great Negator of all experience (emotional, physical, spiritual, and even mental in its positive power), and the only salvation for man is that Urizen be reborn into positive power in the region of artistic experience. He is reborn, in Blake's myth, through the realization of the value of total, integrated experience. Urizen learns that mental dominion is inimical to life and that only through the annihilation of the selfish, partial man can the whole man fulfill his life.

It is significant that Hawthorne discovers man's flaw in the same region of human experience and brings about his redemption through the same act of annihilation. Ethan Brand is a Urizen character in that he falls to a satanic state, realizes his error, annihilates it, and in effect redeems his past sinful life. Just as Urizen, when he becomes Satan, negates the love of Luvah (the emotional Zoa), so Ethan Brand destroys the hearts of others (and also his own). This mind-negation of the heart is the theme of *Ethan Brand*. Hawthorne's "chapter from an abortive romance" is essentially similar in its psychology to the Urizen part of Blake's myth. Satan is incapable of loving or being loved; he is void of feeling and without a feminine emanation (the female counterpart of the Zoa with whom the Zoa must unite before he can attain fulfillment). Ethan Brand thinks he loves but he destroys instead. In the unfolding of Ethan Brand's experience Hawthorne emphasizes also another vital theme of Blake: the imaginative intuition of innocence (in Joe) is contrasted with the obtuseness of adult experience (in Bartram). Blake contrasts these states forcibly in *Songs of Innocence and Experience*. An analysis of the action of *Ethan Brand*, presented parallel with the Urizen action of Blake's myth, shows a significant similarity between the two artists' concepts of the psychology of living. Blake's creation of his mythical character, Urizen, is obviously more detailed and extended to greater length than Hawthorne's creation of Ethan Brand, but the action of Ethan Brand clearly shows him to be a Urizen character. The English poet and the American novelist share a significant community of idea. The parallel here presented shows two nearly contemporary artists presenting, independently, strikingly similar concepts of human psychology.

We may begin with an interpretation of the essential character symbolized in the name of Ethan Brand, who in himself symbolizes the total action of the story: as *ethnos* burning, he in his individual character is symbolic of his own beginning and end. His burning state at the beginning of his quest for "the Unpardonable Sin" can be identified with "the infernal regions" of the kiln when he conceived the "IDEA," just as he identifies himself with the infernal regions at the end. In essence, then, Ethan Brand is a psyche divided into its conscious and unconscious parts. In the beginning he consciously dominated the lives of others, seeking the Unpardonable Sin in them, unconscious of his own satanity; in the end, having realized the Unpardonable Sin in himself, he is conscious of his own satanity and in self-annihilation reveals it to Joe and Bartram, who represent conscious innocence and unconscious experience and who together as father and son constitute a psychic entity objective to Ethan Brand and reacting to him. The reaction, as Hawthorne presents it, is ironic. We should expect innocence to be unconscious, and experience conscious; but little Joe is conscious of Ethan Brand's character, and Bartram unconscious of it. Bartram cannot understand the mute testimony of Ethan Brand's stone heart. His initial evaluation of Ethan Brand indicates the limits of his world: "drunk," which he understands, and "crazy," which he does not. The boy, more perceptive, feels both fear and fascination and sees in the gleam of Ethan Brand's eyes symbolically the fires of the infernal regions of the kiln.

As the action unfolds, Ethan Brand is being consumed by his own mental fires; he returns from his circular journey with the full knowledge of the Unpardonable Sin, having discovered within himself, in his own heart, "The sin of an intellect that triumphed over the sense of brotherhood with man and reverence for God, and sacrificed everything to its own mighty claims!" His end is clear to him: self-annihilation, or more specifically, Satan-annihilation, to free the heart from the mind. Blake also emphasizes this self-judgment: Urizen (the mental Zoa) must free Luvah (the emotional Zoa) from mental dominion before mankind is free. In the beginning of the myth, Satan (the fallen Urizen) negates Luvah (and the other energies of life, too, the spiritual and physical) until he himself is God of all the fallen world. Eventually, however (through a complex of psychic relationships in the myth that have no counterparts in Hawthorne's story), Urizen, realizing the falseness of his Satanic state, annihilates himself (his mental dominion), consumes himself in his mental flames, and thus frees mankind from the bondage of the mind divided from its psychic counterparts.

The first paragraphs of Hawthorne's story establish the dichotomy of the *spirit* worlds, the creative intuition of the innocent child and the drunken obtuseness of the experienced father. We shall find Bartram and the other significant characters of Graylock all identifying their lives with "the black bottle." Only Joe, Bartram's little son, realizes, intuitively, the fiend in the laughter of Ethan Brand whom Bartram can name only as a drunken man, but who the child knows, intuitively again, has returned to enter finally "the infernal regions" of the kiln, which is in no way changed from its state at the time Ethan Brand conceived the IDEA of the Unpardonable Sin. The hell man makes of his life seems everlasting; it has the look of antiquity about it.

Thus the kiln still burns, full of "brands," but, where the solitary tending of the kiln fire produced in Ethan Brand the IDEA, in Bartram it produces nothing of psychic significance; rather it is a "business" only, of production of lime for barter (Bartram), and the light from the fire serves only to contrast for the reader the external figure of the "lime-burner" and the internal state of the "half-frightened child" shrinking from the approach of the fiend who is returning to his "own fireside" where he looks immediately into the fire, both his final resting place and the initial source of the IDEA. Ethan Brand's quest has taken him full circle. He has returned from his search with the answer to his quest; he is sane and sensible and able to tell others the Unpardonable Sin which he discovered within himself.

At this point of the story, Ethan Brand is Blake's Urizen enlightened to his own falseness. The world of Urizen-Satan is entirely objective, and it was in the objective world that Ethan Brand first sought the Unpardonable Sin. Only after years of defeat in his purpose did he discover within himself, in his own heart, what he had set out to seek in others. His terrible laughter is in scorn of himself, at what he sees in his own heart, at his own conduct of life, at his Unpardonable Sin of seeking in others what was from the beginning in him, the sin (most heinous of all) of thinking to the exclusion of feeling. Hawthorne expresses the human worth of Ethan Brand's emotional life in the final revelation: his heart equals a small volume of "special good lime."

Blake is as insistent in revealing the fault of the life of the mind without the heart. In the action among the great Zoas, Luvah (the heart) revolts against Urizen (the mind) and by descending to wrath destroys the mental dominion in Albion (fourfold man, in all his four psychic energies). Ethan Brand's laugh of scorn is his wrath at himself, that is, his mental realization of wrath, at his mental dominion over his own heart which has turned to stone.

Ethan Brand having identified himself, Bartram sends his son off to inform the villagers that Ethan Brand has found the Unpardonable Sin. As soon as the boy leaves, Bartram feels with Ethan Brand a kinship with his crime from which previously the barrier of his son's influence protected him. Fiendish as Ethan Brand is, he effects no evil against the boy, or anyone else, now; all his scorn is against himself. But he has changed from his former ways: when originally he tended the lime kiln, he invoked Satan from it, and between them they framed the act that would result in the Unpardonable Sin. The man and

fiend collaborated in deifying the intellect above all else, and
their success sent Ethan Brand in search of the sin of sins in
others. Now, at the end of the search, we find Ethan Brand no
longer a man but wholly a fiend. When Bartram importunes
him not to bring forth his devil now, Ethan Brand addresses
Bartram as *Man* and asks rhetorically, "What need have I of the
Devil?" He then turns to tend *his* fire, and the stamp of his
character (his *ethos*) is so forcible that even the obtuse Bartram
expects him to "plunge bodily into the flames, and thus vanish from the sight of man."

Now the man and the fiend (both embodied in Ethan Brand)
become involved with imagination and obtuseness. Bartram begins to react to Ethan Brand as Joe had previously reacted. At
this point we recall Bartram's disparaging remark to his son,
"You will never make a man . . ."; Bartram is also curious and
afraid. In these respects he, in the presence of Ethan Brand, enters a state of innocence like the boy's at Ethan Brand's imminent arrival. But Bartram does not long inhabit this imaginative
world so alien to his existence; although he unknowingly identifies correctly Ethan Brand's crime, that his head was turned
[from his heart], he evaluates it incorrectly. Ethan Brand's
fiendishness is the antithesis of madness; Satan always has complete control over his mental powers—his defection is never of
the mind but of the heart; if we do admit a defect in the region
of the mind, the defect is rather a superabundance than a loss
of mind. Thus Bartram, in his obtuseness, fails to see the reality
of Ethan Brand (*ethnos* burning); instead he fears him who
now means no harm, who, more positively, embodies the Unpardonable Sin.

The arrival of the villagers returns the psychological setting
to the *spirit* level of the opening scene; the three characters rep-
resenting the "old acquaintances" of Ethan Brand have spent
their eighteen years drunk with spirits: the "stage-agent," a
"wilted" man; Lawyer Giles, a "fragment of a human being";
the "village doctor," as "savage as a wild beast, and as miserable as a lost soul." Ethan Brand underscores the low state of
thought and feeling of these drunken creatures by his doubt
"whether he had indeed found the Unpardonable Sin, and

found it within himself." These "brute beasts" had shrivelled up their souls with "fiery liquors" as Ethan Brand had hardened his heart with fiery intellect. He rejects them as serving no purpose, even to a fiend; their lives are beyond satanic corruption; but confronted by Esther's father, Ethan Brand quails, reminded once more of his Unpardonable Sin, overshadowed temporarily by the sin of wasted life evidenced by the three drunken villagers. Ethan Brand had negated Esther's heart; his romance was "abortive" no doubt because he could not give (express) his heart, only his mind; Esther is symbolic of all the others whose hearts Ethan Brand negated from fulfilling their expression of love for others.

While Ethan Brand is meditating upon *his* wasted life, Hawthorne presents a panorama of action symbolic of that life, expressed in the theme of the wanderer. The "German Jew" (a wandering Jew) carries on his back the burden of his sin, which is heavy we discover later because of a stone heart within, which may well be indicative of the blow struck at Christ—love, or the heart. The diorama is this burden and symbolically it is Ethan Brand, as its interior subsequently shows.

When the German Jew bids Joe put his head into the box, he is setting the drama of the metamorphosis of Ethan Brand's heart. In youth, Ethan Brand's heart was as "Titanic" and beautiful and potential of imaginative fulfillment as Joe's *head,* but because of Ethan Brand's satanic, intellectual dominion over his heart (and the hearts of others) it has become nothing, or more really, as both fiends (Ethan Brand and the German Jew) can see, a heart of stone. It is Ethan Brand himself who turns his heart to stone, just as he turns the innocent face of Joe to the experience of horror by means of his fiendish stare. The diorama is a most heavy burden now with its weight of this heart of stone—"this Unpardonable Sin!"—and Ethan Brand forewarns us of his inevitable end when he bids his colleague in sin, "Peace . . . or get thee into the furnace yonder," if we complete his thought, "with your diorama on your back."

In yet another area Hawthorne emphasizes Ethan Brand's conduct of life. An old dog, alone in the world, made himself "the object of public notice" as did Ethan Brand. Suddenly the dog, becoming possessed of a demon, travels round and round in pursuit of an unattainable because inadequate *end,* "as if one end of the ridiculous brute's body were at deadly and most unforgivable enmity with the other." Ethan Brand had wandered in a circle, possessed of a demon, his head at enmity with his heart, in pursuit of an unattainable because inadequate end—a life of all mind and no heart.

Ethan Brand himself makes the analogy between himself and the "self-pursuing cur" (although unknowingly at first, he was pursuing the sin in himself), and overwhelmed once more by the enormity of his sin, he breaks into the "awful laugh" that frightens the crowd away and leaves Bartram and Joe alone with their "unwelcome guest," little Joe aware that "some fearful thing" will happen, "for his tender spirit had an intuition of the bleak and terrible loneliness in which this man had enveloped himself." Bartram, however, identified with the "black bottle" acquaintances, is aware of none of the significance of Ethan Brand and his meditations.

In his meditations Ethan Brand relives his becoming a fiend: his original pity, love, and reverence for mankind; his recognition of the heart as a "temple . . . divine"; the ensuing intellectual development which "disturbed the counterpoise between his mind and heart"; the subsequent perishing of the heart under the fiendish eye of "a cold observer," which effected the break in "the magnetic chain of humanity"; the ultimate flowering of the Unpardonable Sin. His quest was a most eminent success, so successful that he has no alternative end; he must return to his burning home.

The "spirits of fire" are his own, the "blue" mental fires of the mind and not the red fires of the heart. He releases Man and Nature of all kinship, on whom he has no claim, because he trampled their great heart beneath his feet, and then embraces "the deadly element of [mental] Fire. . . ." During the remainder of the night, Ethan Brand burns out, disturbing the obtuse Bartram only unconsciously in his dreams, who consciously evaluates the Unpardonable Sin as "humbug."

But Providence and Nature know and rejoice at the revelation of the Unpardonable Sin: the spiritual and the physical,

the sky and the earth, rejoice in the "loftier brotherhood. . . ."
Little Joe is aware of the "sweetness" and light, but Bartram is
concerned only with the fire burned out. His threat to toss
Ethan Brand into the furnace is ironic. The discovery of Ethan
Brand's remains completes the revelation of his character: a
skeleton and heart of snow-white (pure) lime in the attitude of
repose, crumbled into a product for barter by Bartram.

The end of Ethan Brand is specifically consistent with Blake's
Urizen in the state of Satan; in his lowest state, when he is most
devoid of the humanizing feelings of the heart, Satan is petrific.
It is at this state of existence that Hawthorne leaves Ethan
Brand, in the state of the Unpardonable Sin. Ethan Brand discovers in the heart the salvation from the monstrous sin, and
Blake, in the subsequent action of his myth, identifies the ini-
tiation of salvation with the heart—Luvah who, as Orc (Wrath),
destroys the satanic dominion of the mind. Hawthorne implies
Ethan Brand's salvation in his realization of the Unpardonable
Sin within himself. Blake says we carry our heaven and hell
within us; Ethan Brand voluntarily commits his hell to his own
mental fires.

In the act of suicide, Ethan Brand kills the Self that had become satanic in its dominion over other Selfs. In effect, Urizen
kills his Self also when he relinquishes his satanic dominion over
the other Zoas. This freedom from external dominion allows the
individual to pursue his own psychic development. In Blake's
myth, the individual psyche becomes an integrated being in
Golgonooza, the region of artistic living where no Zoa is dominant; the head and heart, the loins and hands (thoughts and
feelings, instincts and intuitions), all experience life together
and become whole together, harmoniously and in proper balance and proportion, depending upon the needs of the individual.

Blake and Hawthorne, as individual artists, portray the necessity to destroy the dominion of the mind in the creative activity. The source of artistic life, or even of a lesser degree of in-
tegration, is negated when the mental faculty is supreme. Ethan
Brand, and Urizen in the fallen state of Satan, are both destructive of creative living, and no positive action can result until

Ethan Brand destroys himself and Urizen gives up his satanic dominion. Only then can the individual act in a state of existence conducive to fulfillment. Blake's Zoas all unite in an artistic, religious life. Hawthorne implies the possibility of fulfillment in the intuitive imagination of Joe, now that Ethan Brand has destroyed the negation of the mind.

Blake essentially identifies religion and art. In a creative life of art, one lives a life of religion. Blake says Jesus is the greatest artist of us all, and in this context, when we live in such a way as to fulfill all our desires harmoniously, allowing no one Zoa-energy to become dominant within us and, perhaps more important, preventing ourselves from negating a fellow psyche outside us, we are becoming more and more Christ-like in our daily lives. Blake intends just such daily living; as religion is not a once-a-week activity, neither is art. In Blake's myth, Albion needs to create each day more nearly perfect than the last, until the moment that time is no more, when the objective world in the revelation of a moment is encompassed within. In this moment of becoming, the individual attains eternal being.

In *Ethan Brand*, Hawthorne explicitly presents the state of mentally dominated existence and implicitly reveals in Joe's imagination the medium of salvation from the faults of man. However, Hawthorne emphasizes the mind-negation of only the heart and imaginative intuition (Esther and little Joe). Ethan Brand negates Esther's heart and his own; he also negates within himself the imaginative intuition that Joe represents for Ethan Brand and all the inhabitants of Graylock whose "spirits" have destroyed them. All of the old generation is dead spiritually; only Joe shows promise of the future when he rejoices with all Nature and Providence at the revelation of the Unpardonable Sin.

Seeing Ethan Brand as a Urizen character elevates the character and action into the condition of a more complete experience involving the religion and psychology of Blake's myth as well as the literary art of Hawthorne's story. This extension of a common reading experience into the wider region of art is an integrating act of which the value increases as quickly as the student's awareness, as if by revelation he sees art as creation and the artist as creator. Thus he realizes in a momentary vision of the complete experience of man that as Ethan Brand is a partial character relative to Albion, so is Albion partial relative to the expression of all art. Whatever art a student experiences increases his conscious awareness of a universe, best expressed in art.

COMMENT

The technique of analysis-synthesis of symbol reveals the identity of art form (idea) in a diversity of individual expression, as artists create or use diverse symbols to express the universal experience of men. This method of study implies that the essence of art is integrity, the wholeness that characterizes the perfection and completeness culminating from continued creativity among artists of all cultures until we see that the word that comes from all tongues is one word. A student may apply this technique to any story that has a symbolic level and thus discover to what extent the story shares the community of artistic expression. However, the value of such close reading is not limited to art; it pervades religion, mythology, psychology, philosophy, and history as well. We have minutely defined the character of Ethan Brand. We discover the same Urizen character in the professor of Walter Van Tilburg Clark's "The Portable Phonograph" and as we continue to analyze character we see that the other three characters fit in essence Blake's other three Zoas and that the four men likewise correspond to Jung's four types of psychological personalities. Hawthorne in "Ethan Brand" exposes one character type intensely; Clark in "The Portable Phonograph" and also in *The Ox-Bow Incident* extends the view over all four character types but with less intensity.

VI

The Secret Sharer

An Episode from the Coast

JOSEPH CONRAD

I

On my right hand there were lines of fishing-stakes resembling a mysterious system of half-submerged bamboo fences, incomprehensible in its division of the domain of tropical fishes, and crazy of aspect as if abandoned for ever by some nomad tribe of fishermen now gone to the other end of the ocean; for there was no sign of human habitation as far as the eye could reach. To the left a group of barren islets, suggesting ruins of stone walls, towers, and blockhouses, had its foundations set in a blue sea that itself looked solid, so still and stable did it lie below my feet; even the track of light from the westering sun shone smoothly, without that animated glitter which tells of an imperceptible ripple. And when I turned my head to take a parting glance at the tug which had just left us anchored outside the bar, I saw the straight line of the flat shore joined to the stable sea, edge to edge, with a perfect and unmarked closeness, in one levelled floor half brown, half blue under the enormous dome of the sky. Corresponding in their insignificance to the islets of the sea, two small clumps of trees, one on each side of the only fault in the impeccable joint, marked the mouth of the river Meinam we had just left on the first preparatory stage of our homeward journey; and, far back on the inland level, a larger and loftier mass, the grove surrounding the great Paknam pagoda, was the only thing on which the eye could rest from the vain task of exploring the monotonous sweep of the horizon. Here and there gleams as of a few scattered pieces of silver marked the windings of the great river; and on the nearest of them, just within the bar, the tug steaming right into the land became lost to my sight, hull and funnel and masts, as though the impassive earth had swallowed her up without an effort, without a tremor. My eye followed the light cloud of her smoke, now here, now there, above the plain, according to the devious curves of the stream, but always fainter and farther away, till I lost it at last behind the mitre-shaped hill of the great pagoda. And then I was left alone with my ship, anchored at the head of the Gulf of Siam.

She floated at the starting-point of a long journey, very still in an immense stillness, the shadows of her spars flung far to the eastward by the setting sun. At that moment I was alone on her decks. There was not a sound in her—and around us nothing moved, nothing lived, not a canoe on the water, not a bird in the air, not a cloud in the sky. In this breathless pause at the threshold of a long passage we seemed to be measuring our fitness for a long and arduous enterprise, the appointed task of both our existences to be carried out, far from all human eyes, with only sky and sea for spectators and for judges.

There must have been some glare in the air to interfere with one's sight, because it was only just before the sun left us that my roaming eyes made out beyond the highest ridge of the principal islet of the group something which did away with the solemnity of perfect solitude. The tide of darkness flowed on swiftly; and with tropical suddenness a swarm of stars came out above the shadowy earth, while I lingered yet, my hand resting lightly on my ship's rail as if on the shoulder of a trusted friend. But, with all that multitude of celestial bodies staring down at one, the comfort of quiet communion with her was gone for good. And there were also disturbing sounds by this time— voices, footsteps forward; the steward flitted along the maindeck, a busily ministering spirit; a hand-bell tinkled urgently under the poop-deck. . . .

I found my two officers waiting for me near the supper table, in the lighted cuddy. We sat down at once, and as I helped the chief mate, I said:

"Are you aware that there is a ship anchored inside the islands? I saw her mastheads above the ridge as the sun went down."

He raised sharply his simple face, overcharged by a terrible growth of whisker, and emitted his usual ejaculations: "Bless my soul, sir! You don't say so!"

My second mate was a round-cheeked, silent young man, grave beyond his years, I thought; but as our eyes happened to meet I detected a slight quiver on his lips. I looked down at once. It was not my part to encourage sneering on board my ship. It must be said, too, that I knew very little of my officers. In consequence of certain events of no particular significance, except to myself, I had been appointed to the command only a fortnight before. Neither did I know much of the hands forward. All these people had been together for eighteen months or so, and my position was that of the only stranger on board. I mention this because it has some bearing on what is to follow. But what I felt most was my being a stranger to the ship; and if all the truth must be told, I was somewhat of a stranger to myself. The youngest man on board (barring the second mate), and untried as yet by a position of the fullest responsibility, I was willing to take the adequacy of the others for granted. They had simply to be equal to their tasks; but I wondered how far I should turn out faithful to that ideal conception of one's own personality every man sets up for himself secretly.

Meantime the chief mate, with an almost visible effect of collaboration on the part of his round eyes and frightful whiskers, was trying to evolve a theory of the anchored ship. His dominant trait was to take all things into earnest consideration. He was of a painstaking turn of mind. As he used to say, he "liked to account to himself" for practically everything that came in his way, down to a miserable scorpion he had found in his cabin a week before. The why and the wherefore of that scorpion —how it got on board and came to select his room rather than the pantry (which was a dark place and more what a scorpion would be partial to), and how on earth it managed to drown itself in the inkwell of his writing-desk—had exercised him infinitely. The ship within the islands was much more easily accounted for; and just as we were about to rise from table he made his pronouncement. She was, he doubted not, a ship from home lately arrived. Probably she drew too much water to cross the bar except at the top of spring tides. Therefore she went into that natural harbour to wait for a few days in preference to remaining in an open roadstead.

"That's so," confirmed the second mate, suddenly, in his slightly hoarse voice. "She draws over twenty feet. She's the Liverpool ship *Sephora* with a cargo of coal. Hundred and twenty-three days from Cardiff."

We looked at him in surprise.

"The tugboat skipper told me when he came on board for your letters, sir," explained the young man. "He expects to take her up the river the day after tomorrow."

After thus overwhelming us with the extent of his information he slipped out of the cabin. The mate observed regretfully that he "could not account for that young fellow's whims." What prevented him telling us all about it at once, he wanted to know.

I detained him as he was making a move. For the last two days the crew had had plenty of hard work, and the night before they had very little sleep. I felt painfully that I—a stranger —was doing something unusual when I directed him to let all hands turn in without setting an anchor-watch. I proposed to keep on deck myself till one o'clock or thereabouts. I would get the second mate to relieve me at that hour.

"He will turn out the cook and the steward at four," I concluded, "and then give you a call. Of course at the slightest sign of any sort of wind we'll have the hands up and make a start at once."

He concealed his astonishment. "Very well, sir." Outside the cuddy he put his head in the second mate's door to inform him of my unheard-of caprice to take a five hours' anchor-watch on myself. I heard the other raise his voice incredulously—"What?

The Captain himself?" Then a few more murmurs, a door closed, then another. A few moments later I went on deck.

My strangeness, which had made me sleepless, had prompted that unconventional arrangement, as if I had expected in those solitary hours of the night to get on terms with the ship of which I knew nothing, manned by men of whom I knew very little more. Fast alongside a wharf, littered like any ship in port with a tangle of unrelated things, invaded by unrelated shore people, I had hardly seen her yet properly. Now, as she lay cleared for sea, the stretch of her main-deck seemed to me very fine under the stars. Very fine, very roomy for her size, and very inviting. I descended the poop and paced the waist, my mind picturing to myself the coming passage through the Malay Archipelago, down the Indian Ocean, and up the Atlantic. All its phases were familiar enough to me, every characteristic, all the alternatives which were likely to face me on the high seas—everything! . . . except the novel responsibility of command. But I took heart from the reasonable thought that the ship was like other ships, the men like other men, and that the sea was not likely to keep any special surprises expressly for my discomfiture.

Arrived at that comforting conclusion, I bethought myself of a cigar and went below to get it. All was still down there. Everybody at the after end of the ship was sleeping profoundly. I came out again on the quarter-deck, agreeably at ease in my sleeping-suit on that warm breathless night, barefooted, a glowing cigar in my teeth, and, going forward, I was met by the profound silence of the fore end of the ship. Only as I passed the door of the forecastle I heard a deep, quiet, trustful sigh of some sleeper inside. And suddenly I rejoiced in the great security of the sea as compared with the unrest of the land, in my choice of that untempted life presenting no disquieting problems, invested with an elementary moral beauty by the absolute straightforwardness of its appeal and by the singleness of its purpose.

The riding-light in the fore-rigging burned with a clear, untroubled, as if symbolic, flame, confident and bright in the mysterious shades of the night. Passing on my way aft along the other side of the ship, I observed that the rope side-ladder, put over, no doubt, for the master of the tug when he came to fetch away our letters, had not been hauled in as it should have been. I became annoyed at this, for exactitude in small matters is the very soul of discipline. Then I reflected that I had myself peremptorily dismissed my officers from duty, and by my own act had prevented the anchor-watch being formally set and things properly attended to. I asked myself whether it was wise ever to interfere with the established routine of duties even from the kindest of motives. My action might have made me appear eccentric. Goodness only knew how that absurdly whiskered mate would "account" for my conduct, and what the whole ship thought of that informality of their new captain. I was vexed with myself.

Not from compunction certainly, but, as it were mechanically, I proceeded to get the ladder in myself. Now a side-ladder of that sort is a light affair and comes in easily, yet my vigorous tug, which should have brought it flying on board, merely recoiled upon my body in a totally unexpected jerk. What the devil! . . . I was so astounded by the immovableness of that ladder that I remained stock-still, trying to account for it to myself like that imbecile mate of mine. In the end, of course, I put my head over the rail.

The side of the ship made an opaque belt of shadow on the darkling glassy shimmer of the sea. But I saw at once something elongated and pale floating very close to the ladder. Before I could form a guess a faint flash of phosphorescent light, which seemed to issue suddenly from the naked body of a man, flickered in the sleeping water with the elusive, silent play of summer lightning in a night sky. With a gasp I saw revealed to my stare a pair of feet, the long legs, a broad livid back immersed right up to the neck in a greenish cadaverous glow. One hand, awash, clutched the bottom rung of the ladder. He was complete but for the head. A headless corpse! The cigar dropped out of my gaping mouth with a tiny plop and a short hiss quite audible in the absolute stillness of all things under heaven. At that I suppose he raised up his face, a dimly pale oval in the shadow of the ship's side. But even then I could only barely make out down there the shape of his black-haired head. However, it was enough for the horrid, frost-bound sensation which had gripped me about the chest to pass off. The moment of vain exclamations was past, too. I only climbed on the spare spar and leaned over the rail as far as I could, to bring my eyes nearer to that mystery floating alongside.

As he hung by the ladder, like a resting swimmer, the sea-lightning played about his limbs at every stir; and he appeared in it ghastly, silvery, fish-like. He remained as mute as a fish, too. He made no motion to get out of the water, either. It was inconceivable that he should not attempt to come on board, and strangely troubling to suspect that perhaps he did not want to. And my first words were prompted by just that troubled incertitude.

"What's the matter?" I asked in my ordinary tone, speaking down to the face upturned exactly under mine.

"Cramp," it answered, no louder. Then slightly anxious, "I say, no need to call any one."

"I was not going to," I said.

"Are you alone on deck?"

"Yes."

I had somehow the impression that he was on the point of letting go the ladder to swim away beyond my ken—mysterious as he came. But, for the moment, this being appearing as if he had risen from the bottom of the sea (it was certainly the nearest land to the ship) wanted only to know the time. I told him. And he, down there, tentatively:

"I suppose your captain's turned in?"

"I am sure he isn't," I said.

He seemed to struggle with himself, for I heard something like the low, bitter murmur of doubt. "What's the good?" His next words came out with a hesitating effort.

"Look here, my man. Could you call him out quietly?"

I thought the time had come to declare myself.

"*I* am the captain."

I heard a "By Jove!" whispered at the level of the water. The

phosphorescence flashed in the swirl of the water all about his
limbs, his other hand seized the ladder.

"My name's Leggatt."

The voice was calm and resolute. A good voice. The self-pos-
session of that man had somehow induced a corresponding state
in myself. It was very quietly that I remarked:

"You must be a good swimmer."

"Yes. I've been in the water practically since nine o'clock.
The question for me now is whether I am to let go this ladder
and go on swimming till I sink from exhaustion, or—to come
on board here."

I felt this was no mere formula of desperate speech, but a
real alternative in the view of a strong soul. I should have
gathered from this that he was young; indeed, it is only the
young who are ever confronted by such clear issues. But at the
time it was pure intuition on my part. A mysterious communication was established already between us two—in the face of
that silent, darkened tropical sea. I was young, too; young
enough to make no comment. The man in the water began suddenly to climb up the ladder, and I hastened away from the rail
to fetch some clothes.

Before entering the cabin I stood still, listening in the lobby
at the foot of the stairs. A faint snore came through the closed
door of the chief mate's room. The second mate's door was on
the hook, but the darkness in there was absolutely soundless. He,
too, was young and could sleep like a stone. Remained the steward, but he was not likely to wake up before he was called. I got
a sleeping-suit out of my room and, coming back on deck, saw
the naked man from the sea sitting on the main-hatch, glim-
mering white in the darkness, his elbows on his knees and his
head in his hands. In a moment he had concealed his damp
body in a sleeping-suit of the same grey-stripe pattern as the one
I was wearing and followed me like my double on the poop. Together we moved right aft, barefooted, silent.

"What is it?" I asked in a deadened voice, taking the lighted
lamp out of the binnacle, and raising it to his face.

"An ugly business."

He had rather regular features; a good mouth; light eyes under somewhat heavy, dark eyebrows; a smooth, square forehead; no growth on his cheeks; a small, brown moustache, and a well-shaped, round chin. His expression was concentrated, meditative, under the inspecting light of the lamp I held up to his face; such as a man thinking hard in solitude might wear. My sleeping-suit was just right for his size. A well-knit young fellow of twenty-five at most. He caught his lower lip with the edge of white, even teeth.

"Yes," I said, replacing the lamp in the binnacle. The warm, heavy tropical night closed upon his head again.

"There's a ship over there," he murmured.

"Yes, I know. The *Sephora*. Did you know of us?"

"Hadn't the slightest idea. I am the mate of her——" He paused and corrected himself. "I should say I *was*."

"Aha! Something wrong?"

"Yes. Very wrong indeed. I've killed a man."

"What do you mean? Just now?"

"No, on the passage. Weeks ago. Thirty-nine south. When I say a man——"

"Fit of temper," I suggested, confidently.

The shadowy, dark head, like mine, seemed to nod imperceptibly above the ghostly grey of my sleeping-suit. It was, in the night, as though I had been faced by my own reflection in the depths of a sombre and immense mirror.

"A pretty thing to have to own up to for a Conway boy," murmured my double, distinctly.

"You're a Conway boy?"

"I am," he said, as if startled. Then, slowly . . . "Perhaps you too——"

It was so; but being a couple of years older I had left before he joined. After a quick interchange of dates a silence fell; and I thought suddenly of my absurd mate with his terrific whiskers and the "Bless my soul—you don't say so" type of intellect. My double gave me an inkling of his thoughts by saying: "My father's a parson in Norfolk. Do you see me before a judge and jury on that charge? For myself I can't see the necessity. There are fellows that an angel from heaven——And I am not that. He was one of those creatures that are just simmering all the time

with a silly sort of wickedness. Miserable devils that have no
business to live at all. He wouldn't do his duty and wouldn't let
anybody else do theirs. But what's the good of talking! You know
well enough the sort of ill-conditioned snarling cur——"

He appealed to me as if our experiences had been as identical as our clothes. And I knew well enough the pestiferous danger of such a character where there are no means of legal repression. And I knew well enough also that my double there
was no homicidal ruffian. I did not think of asking him for details, and he told me the story roughly in brusque, disconnected
sentences. I needed no more. I saw it all going on as though I
were myself inside that other sleeping-suit.

"It happened while we were setting a reefed foresail, at dusk.
Reefed foresail! You understand the sort of weather. The only
sail we had left to keep the ship running; so you may guess what
it had been like for days. Anxious sort of job, that. He gave me
some of his cursed insolence at the sheet. I tell you I was overdone with this terrific weather that seemed to have no end to
it. Terrific, I tell you—and a deep ship. I believe the fellow himself was half crazed with funk. It was no time for gentlemanly
reproof, so I turned round and felled him like an ox. He up and
at me. We closed just as an awful sea made for the ship. All
hands saw it coming and took to the rigging, but I had him by
the throat, and went on shaking him like a rat, the men above
us yelling, 'Look out! look out!' Then a crash as if the sky had
fallen on my head. They say that for over ten minutes hardly
anything was to be seen of the ship—just the three masts and a
bit of the forecastle head and of the poop all awash driving
along in a smother of foam. It was a miracle that they found us,
jammed together behind the forebits. It's clear that I meant business, because I was holding him by the throat still when they
picked us up. He was black in the face. It was too much for
them. It seems they rushed us aft together, gripped as we were,
screaming 'Murder!' like a lot of lunatics, and broke into the
cuddy. And the ship running for her life, touch and go all the
time, any minute her last in a sea fit to turn your hair grey only
a-looking at it. I understand that the skipper, too, started raving
like the rest of them. The man had been deprived of sleep for
more than a week, and to have this sprung on him at the height

of a furious gale nearly drove him out of his mind. I wonder they didn't fling me overboard after getting the carcass of their precious ship-mate out of my fingers. They had rather a job to separate us, I've been told. A sufficiently fierce story to make an old judge and a respectable jury sit up a bit. The first thing I heard when I came to myself was the maddening howling of that endless gale, and on that the voice of the old man. He was hanging on to my bunk, staring into my face out of his sou'wester.

" 'Mr. Leggatt, you have killed a man. You can act no longer as chief mate of this ship.' "

His care to subdue his voice made it sound monotonous. He rested a hand on the end of the skylight to steady himself with, and all that time did not stir a limb, so far as I could see. "Nice little tale for a quiet tea-party," he concluded in the same tone.

One of my hands, too, rested on the end of the skylight; neither did I stir a limb, so far as I knew. We stood less than a foot from each other. It occurred to me that if old "Bless my soul—you don't say so" were to put his head up the companion and catch sight of us, he would think he was seeing double, or imagine himself come upon a scene of weird witchcraft; the strange captain having a quiet confabulation by the wheel with his own grey ghost. I became very much concerned to prevent anything of the sort. I heard the other's soothing undertone.

"My father's a parson in Norfolk," it said. Evidently he had forgotten he had told me this important fact before. Truly a nice little tale.

"You had better slip down into my stateroom now," I said, moving off stealthily. My double followed my movements; our bare feet made no sound; I let him in, closed the door with care, and, after giving a call to the second mate, returned on deck for my relief.

"Not much sign of any wind yet," I remarked when he approached.

"No, sir. Not much," he assented, sleepily, in his hoarse voice, with just enough deference, no more, and barely suppressing a yawn.

"Well, that's all you have to look out for. You have got your orders."

"Yes, sir."

I paced a turn or two on the poop and saw him take up his position face forward with his elbow in the ratlines of the mizzen-rigging before I went below. The mate's faint snoring was still going on peacefully. The cuddy lamp was burning over the table on which stood a vase with flowers, a polite attention from the ship's provision merchant—the last flowers we should see for the next three months at the very least. Two bunches of bananas hung from the beam symmetrically, one on each side of the rudder-casing. Everything was as before in the ship—except that two of her captain's sleeping-suits were simultaneously in use, one motionless in the cuddy, the other keeping very still in the captain's stateroom.

It must be explained here that my cabin had the form of the capital letter L the door being within the angle and opening into the short part of the letter. A couch was to the left, the bed-place to the right; my writing-desk and the chronometers' table faced the door. But any one opening it, unless he stepped right inside, had no view of what I call the long (or vertical) part of the letter. It contained some lockers surmounted by a bookcase; and a few clothes, a thick jacket or two, caps, oilskin coat, and such like, hung on hooks. There was at the bottom of that part a door opening into my bath-room, which could be entered also directly from the saloon. But that way was never used.

The mysterious arrival had discovered the advantage of this particular shape. Entering my room, lighted strongly by a big bulkhead lamp swung on gimbals above my writing-desk, I did not see him anywhere till he stepped out quietly from behind the coats hung in the recessed part.

"I heard somebody moving about, and went in there at once," he whispered.

I, too, spoke under my breath.

"Nobody is likely to come in here without knocking and getting permission."

He nodded. His face was thin and the sunburn faded, as though he had been ill. And no wonder. He had been, I heard presently, kept under arrest in his cabin for nearly seven weeks. But there was nothing sickly in his eyes or in his expression. He was not a bit like me, really; yet, as we stood leaning over my bed-place, whispering side by side, with our dark heads together and our backs to the door, anybody bold enough to open it stealthily would have been treated to the uncanny sight of a double captain busy talking in whispers with his other self.

"But all this doesn't tell me how you came to hang on to our side-ladder," I inquired, in the hardly audible murmurs we used, after he had told me something more of the proceedings on board the *Sephora* once the bad weather was over.

"When we sighted Java Head I had had time to think all those matters out several times over. I had six weeks of doing nothing else, and with only an hour or so every evening for a tramp on the quarter-deck."

He whispered, his arms folded on the side of my bed-place, staring through the open port. And I could imagine perfectly the manner of this thinking out—a stubborn if not a steadfast operation; something of which I should have been perfectly incapable.

"I reckoned it would be dark before we closed with the land," he continued, so low that I had to strain my hearing, near as we were to each other, shoulder touching shoulder almost. "So I asked to speak to the old man. He always seemed very sick when he came to see me—as if he could not look me in the face. You know, that foresail saved the ship. She was too deep to have run long under bare poles. And it was I that managed to set it for him. Anyway, he came. When I had him in my cabin—he stood by the door looking at me as if I had the halter round my neck already—I asked him right away to leave my cabin door unlocked at night while the ship was going through Sunda Straits. There would be the Java coast within two or three miles, off Angier Point. I wanted nothing more. I've had a prize for swimming my second year in the Conway."

"I can believe it," I breathed out.

"God only knows why they locked me in every night. To see some of their faces you'd have thought they were afraid I'd go about at night strangling people. Am I a murdering brute? Do I look it? By Jove! if I had been he wouldn't have trusted himself like that into my room. You'll say I might have chucked him aside and bolted out, there and then—it was dark already.

Well, no. And for the same reason I wouldn't think of trying to smash the door. There would have been a rush to stop me at the noise, and I did not mean to get into a confounded scrimmage. Somebody else might have got killed—for I would not have broken out only to get chucked back, and I did not want any more of that work. He refused, looking more sick than ever. He was afraid of the men, and also of that old second mate of his who had been sailing with him for years—a grey-headed old humbug; and his steward, too, had been with him devil knows how long—seventeen years or more—a dogmatic sort of loafer who hated me like poison, just because I was the chief mate. No chief mate ever made more than one voyage in the *Sephora,* you know. Those two old chaps ran the ship. Devil only knows what the skipper wasn't afraid of (all his nerve went to pieces altogether in that hellish spell of bad weather we had)—of what the law would do to him—of his wife, perhaps. Oh, yes! she's on board. Though I don't think she would have meddled. She would have been only too glad to have me out of the ship in any way. The 'brand of Cain' business, don't you see. That's all right. I was ready enough to go off wandering on the face of the earth—and that was price enough to pay for an Abel of that sort. Anyhow, he wouldn't listen to me. 'This thing must take its course. I represent the law here.' He was shaking like a leaf. 'So you won't?' 'No!' 'Then I hope you will be able to sleep on that,' I said, and turned my back on him. 'I wonder that *you* can,' cries he, and locks the door.

"Well, after that, I couldn't. Not very well. That was three weeks ago. We have had a slow passage through the Java Sea; drifted about Carimata for ten days. When we anchored here they thought, I suppose, it was all right. The nearest land (and that's five miles) is the ship's destination; the consul would soon set about catching me; and there would have been no object in bolting to these islets there. I don't suppose there's a drop of water on them. I don't know how it was, but to-night that steward, after bringing me my supper, went out to let me eat it, and left the door unlocked. And I ate it—all there was, too. After I had finished I strolled out on the quarter-deck. I don't know that I meant to do anything. A breath of fresh air was all I wanted, I believe. Then a sudden temptation came over me. I kicked off my slippers and was in the water before I had made up my mind fairly. Somebody heard the splash and they raised an awful hullabaloo. 'He's gone! Lower the boats! He's committed suicide! No, he's swimming.' Certainly I was swimming. It's not so easy for a swimmer like me to commit suicide by drowning. I landed on the nearest islet before the boat left the ship's side. I heard them pulling about in the dark, hailing, and so on, but after a bit they gave up. Everything quieted down and the anchorage became as still as death. I sat down on a stone and began to think. I felt certain they would start searching for me at daylight. There was no place to hide on those stony things—and if there had been, what would have been the good? But now I was clear of that ship, I was not going back. So after a while I took off all my clothes, tied them up in a bundle with a stone inside, and dropped them in the deep water on the outer side of that islet. That was suicide enough for me. Let them think what they liked, but I didn't mean to drown myself. I meant to swim till I sank—but that's not the same thing. I struck out for another of these little islands, and it was from that one that I first saw your riding-light. Something to swim for. I went on easily, and on the way I came upon a flat rock a foot or two above water. In the daytime, I dare say, you might make it out with a glass from your poop. I scrambled up on it and rested myself for a bit. Then I made another start. That last spell must have been over a mile."

His whisper was getting fainter and fainter, and all the time he stared straight out through the port-hole, in which there was not even a star to be seen. I had not interrupted him. There was something that made comment impossible in his narrative, or perhaps in himself; a sort of feeling, a quality, which I can't find a name for. And when he ceased, all I found was a futile whisper: "So you swam for our light?"

"Yes—straight for it. It was something to swim for. I couldn't see any stars low down because the coast was in the way, and I couldn't see the land, either. The water was like glass. One might have been swimming in a confounded thousand-feet deep cistern with no place for scrambling out anywhere; but what I didn't like was the notion of swimming round and round like a crazed bullock before I gave out; and as I didn't mean to go back . . . No. Do you see me being hauled back, stark naked, off one of these little islands by the scruff of the neck and fighting like a wild beast? Somebody would have got killed for certain, and I did not want any of that. So I went on. Then your ladder——"

"Why didn't you hail the ship?" I asked, a little louder.

He touched my shoulder lightly. Lazy footsteps came right over our heads and stopped. The second mate had crossed from the other side of the poop and might have been hanging over the rail, for all we knew.

"He couldn't hear us talking—could he?" My double breathed into my very ear, anxiously.

His anxiety was an answer, a sufficient answer, to the question I had put to him. An answer containing all the difficulty of that situation. I closed the port-hole quietly, to make sure. A louder word might have been overheard.

"Who's that?" he whispered then.

"My second mate. But I don't know much more of the fellow than you do."

And I told him a little about myself. I had been appointed to take charge while I least expected anything of the sort, not quite a fortnight ago. I didn't know either the ship or the people. Hadn't had the time in port to look about me or size anybody up. And as to the crew, all they knew was that I was appointed to take the ship home. For the rest, I was almost as much of a stranger on board as himself, I said. And at the moment I felt it most acutely. I felt that it would take very little to make me a suspect person in the eyes of the ship's company.

He had turned about meantime; and we, the two strangers in the ship, faced each other in identical attitudes.

"Your ladder——" he murmured, after a silence. "Who'd have thought of finding a ladder hanging over at night in a ship anchored out here! I felt just then a very unpleasant faintness. After the life I've been leading for nine weeks, anybody would have got out of condition. I wasn't capable of swimming round as far as your rudder-chains. And, lo and behold! there was a ladder to get hold of. After I gripped it I said to myself, 'What's the good?' When I saw a man's head looking over I thought I would swim away presently and leave him shouting—in whatever language it was. I didn't mind being looked at. I—I liked it. And then you speaking to me so quietly—as if you had expected me—made me hold on a little longer. It had been a confounded lonely time—I don't mean while swimming. I was glad to talk a little to somebody that didn't belong to the *Sephora.* As to asking for the captain, that was a mere impulse. It could have been no use, with all the ship knowing about me and the other people pretty certain to be round here in the morning. I don't know—I wanted to be seen, to talk with somebody, before I went on. I don't know what I would have said. . . . 'Fine night, isn't it?' or something of the sort."

"Do you think they will be round here presently?" I asked with some incredulity.

"Quite likely," he said, faintly.

He looked extremely haggard all of a sudden. His head rolled on his shoulders.

"H'm. We shall see then. Meantime get into that bed," I whispered. "Want help? There."

It was a rather high bed-place with a set of drawers underneath. This amazing swimmer really needed the lift I gave him by seizing his leg. He tumbled in, rolled over on his back, and flung one arm across his eyes. And then, with his face nearly hidden, he must have looked exactly as I used to look in that bed. I gazed upon my other self for a while before drawing across carefully the two green serge curtains which ran on a brass rod. I thought for a moment of pinning them together for greater safety, but I sat down on the couch, and once there I felt unwilling to rise and hunt for a pin. I would do it in a moment. I was extremely tired, in a peculiarly intimate way, by the strain of stealthiness, by the effort of whispering and the general secrecy of this excitement. It was three o'clock by now and I had been on my feet since nine, but I was not sleepy; I could not have gone to sleep. I sat there, fagged out, looking at the curtains, trying to clear my mind of the confused sensation of being in two places at once, and greatly bothered by an exasperating knocking in my head. It was a relief to discover suddenly that it was not in my head at all, but on the outside of the door. Before I could collect myself the words "Come in" were out of my mouth, and the steward entered with a tray, bringing in my morning coffee. I had slept, after all, and I was so frightened that I shouted, "This way! I am here, steward," as though he had been miles away. He put down the tray on the table next the couch and only then said, very quietly, "I can see you are here, sir." I felt him give me a keen look, but I dared not meet his eyes just then. He must have wondered why I had drawn the curtains of my bed before going to sleep on the couch. He went out, hooking the door open as usual.

I heard the crew washing decks above me. I knew I would have been told at once if there had been any wind. Calm, I thought, and I was doubly vexed. Indeed, I felt dual more than ever. The steward reappeared suddenly in the doorway. I jumped up from the couch so quickly that he gave a start.

"What do you want here?"

"Close your port, sir—they are washing decks."

"It is closed," I said, reddening.

"Very well, sir." But he did not move from the doorway and returned my stare in an extraordinary, equivocal manner for a time. Then his eyes wavered, all his expression changed, and in a voice unusually gentle, almost coaxingly:

"May I come in to take the empty cup away, sir?"

"Of course!" I turned my back on him while he popped in and out. Then I unhooked and closed the door and even pushed the bolt. This sort of thing could not go on very long. The cabin was as hot as an oven, too. I took a peep at my double, and discovered that he had not moved, his arm was still over his eyes; but his chest heaved; his hair was wet; his chin glistened with perspiration. I reached over him and opened the port.

"I must show myself on deck," I reflected.

Of course, theoretically, I could do what I liked, with no one to say nay to me within the whole circle of the horizon; but to lock my cabin door and take the key away I did not dare. Directly I put my head out of the companion I saw the group of my two officers, the second mate barefooted, the chief mate in long india-rubber boots, near the break of the poop, and the steward half-way down the poop-ladder talking to them eagerly. He happened to catch sight of me and dived, the second ran down on the main-deck shouting some order or other, and the chief mate came to meet me, touching his cap.

There was a sort of curiosity in his eye that I did not like. I don't know whether the steward had told them that I was "queer" only, or downright drunk, but I know the man meant to have a good look at me. I watched him coming with a smile which, as he got into point-blank range, took effect and froze his very whiskers. I did not give him time to open his lips.

"Square the yards by lifts and braces before the hands go to breakfast."

It was the first particular order I had given on board that ship; and I stayed on deck to see it executed, too. I had felt the need of asserting myself without loss of time. That sneering young cub got taken down a peg or two on that occasion, and I also seized the opportunity of having a good look at the face of every foremast man as they filed past me to go to the after braces. At breakfast time, eating nothing myself, I presided with such frigid dignity that the two mates were only too glad to escape from the cabin as soon as decency permitted; and all the time the dual working of my mind distracted me almost to the point of insanity. I was constantly watching myself, my secret self, as dependent on my actions as my own personality, sleeping in that bed, behind that door which faced me as I sat at the head of the table. It was very much like being mad, only it was worse because one was aware of it.

I had to shake him for a solid minute, but when at last he opened his eyes it was in the full possession of his senses, with an inquiring look.

"All's well so far," I whispered. "Now you must vanish into the bath-room."

He did so, as noiseless as a ghost, and then I rang for the steward, and facing him boldly, directed him to tidy up my stateroom while I was having my bath—"and be quick about it." As my tone admitted of no excuses, he said, "Yes, sir," and ran off to fetch his dust-pan and brushes. I took a bath and did most of my dressing, splashing, and whistling softly for the steward's edification, while the secret sharer of my life stood drawn up bolt upright in that little space, his face looking very sunken in daylight, his eyelids lowered under the stern, dark line of his eyebrows drawn together by a slight frown.

When I left him there to go back to my room the steward was finishing dusting. I sent for the mate and engaged him in some insignificant conversation. It was, as it were, trifling with the terrific character of his whiskers; but my object was to give him an opportunity for a good look at my cabin. And then I could at last shut, with a clear conscience, the door of my stateroom and get my double back into the recessed part. There was nothing else for it. He had to sit still on a small folding stool, half smothered by the heavy coats hanging there. We listened to the steward going into the bath-room out of the saloon, filling the water-bottles there, scrubbing the bath, setting things to rights, whisk, bang, clatter—out again into the saloon—turn the key—click. Such was my scheme for keeping my second self invisible. Nothing better could be contrived under the circumstances. And there we sat; I at my writing-desk ready to appear busy with some papers, he behind me out of sight of the door. It would not have been prudent to talk in daytime; and I could not have stood the excitement of that queer sense of whispering to myself. Now and then, glancing over my shoulder, I saw him far back there, sitting rigidly on the low stool, his bare feet close together, his arms folded, his head hanging on his breast—and perfectly still. Anybody would have taken him for me.

I was fascinated by it myself. Every moment I had to glance over my shoulder. I was looking at him when a voice outside the door said:

"Beg pardon, sir."

"Well!" . . . I kept my eyes on him, and so when the voice outside the door announced, "There's a ship's boat coming our way, sir," I saw him give a start—the first movement he had made for hours. But he did not raise his bowed head.

"All right. Get the ladder over."

I hesitated. Should I whisper something to him? But what?

His immobility seemed to have been never disturbed. What could I tell him he did not know already? . . . Finally I went on deck.

II

The skipper of the *Sephora* had a thin red whisker all round his face, and the sort of complexion that goes with hair of that colour; also the particular, rather smeary shade of blue in the eyes. He was not exactly a showy figure; his shoulders were high, his stature but middling—one leg slightly more bandy than the other. He shook hands, looking vaguely around. A spiritless tenacity was his main characteristic, I judged. I behaved with a politeness which seemed to disconcert him. Perhaps he was shy. He mumbled to me as if he were ashamed of what he was saying; gave his name (it was something like Archbold—but at this distance of years I hardly am sure), his ship's name, and a few other particulars of that sort, in the manner of a criminal making a reluctant and doleful confession. He had had terrible weather on the passage out—terrible—terrible—wife aboard, too.

By this time we were seated in the cabin and the steward brought in a tray with a bottle and glasses. "Thanks! No." Never took liquor. Would have some water, though. He drank two tumblerfuls. Terrible thirsty work. Ever since daylight had been exploring the islands round his ship.

"What was that for—fun?" I asked, with an appearance of polite interest.

"No!" He sighed. "Painful duty."

As he persisted in his mumbling and I wanted my double to hear every word, I hit upon the notion of informing him that I regretted to say I was hard of hearing.

"Such a young man, too!" he nodded, keeping his smeary blue, unintelligent eyes fastened upon me. "What was the cause of it—some disease?" he inquired, without the least sympathy and as if he thought that, if so, I'd got no more than I deserved.

"Yes; disease," I admitted in a cheerful tone which seemed to shock him. But my point was gained, because he had to raise his voice to give me his tale. It is not worth while to record that version. It was just over two months since all this had happened, and he had thought so much about it that he seemed completely muddled as to its bearings, but still immensely impressed.

"What would you think of such a thing happening on board your own ship? I've had the *Sephora* for these fifteen years. I am a well-known shipmaster."

He was densely distressed—and perhaps I should have sympathised with him if I had been able to detach my mental vision from the unsuspected sharer of my cabin as though he were my second self. There he was on the other side of the bulkhead, four or five feet from us, no more, as we sat in the saloon. I looked politely at Captain Archbold (if that was his name), but it was the other I saw, in a grey sleeping-suit, seated on a low stool, his bare feet close together, his arms folded, and every word said between us falling into the ears of his dark head bowed on his chest.

"I have been at sea now, man and boy, for seven-and-thirty years, and I've never heard of such a thing happening in an English ship. And that it should be my ship. Wife on board, too."

I was hardly listening to him.

"Don't you think," I said, "that the heavy sea which, you told me, came aboard just then might have killed the man? I have seen the sheer weight of a sea kill a man very neatly, by simply breaking his neck."

"Good God!" he uttered, impressively, fixing his smeary blue eyes on me. "The sea! No man killed by the sea ever looked like that." He seemed positively scandalised at my suggestion. And as I gazed at him, certainly not prepared for anything original on his part, he advanced his head close to mine and thrust his tongue out at me so suddenly that I couldn't help starting back.

After scoring over my calmness in this graphic way he nodded wisely. If I had seen the sight, he assured me, I would never forget it as long as I lived. The weather was too bad to give the corpse a proper sea burial. So next day at dawn they took it up on the poop, covering its face with a bit of bunting; he read a short prayer, and then, just as it was, in its oilskins and long boots, they launched it amongst those mountainous seas that seemed ready every moment to swallow up the ship herself and the terrified lives on board of her.

"That reefed foresail saved you," I threw in.

"Under God—it did," he exclaimed fervently. "It was by a special mercy, I firmly believe, that it stood some of those hurricane squalls."

"It was the setting of that sail which——" I began.

"God's own hand in it," he interrupted me. "Nothing less could have done it. I don't mind telling you that I hardly dared give the order. It seemed impossible that we could touch anything without losing it, and then our last hope would have been gone."

The terror of that gale was on him yet. I let him go on for a bit, then said, casually—as if returning to a minor subject:

"You were very anxious to give up your mate to the shore people, I believe?"

He was. To the law. His obscure tenacity on that point had in it something incomprehensible and a little awful; something, as it were, mystical, quite apart from his anxiety that he should not be suspected of "countenancing any doings of that sort." Seven-and-thirty virtuous years at sea, of which over twenty of immaculate command, and the last fifteen in the *Sephora,* seemed to have laid him under some pitiless obligation.

"And you know," he went on, groping shamefacedly amongst his feelings, "I did not engage that young fellow. His people had some interest with my owners. I was in a way forced to take him on. He looked very smart, very gentlemanly, and all that. But do you know—I never liked him, somehow. I am a plain man. You see, he wasn't exactly the sort for the chief mate of a ship like the *Sephora.*"

I had become so connected in thoughts and impressions with the secret sharer of my cabin that I felt as if I, personally, were being given to understand that I, too, was not the sort that would have done for the chief mate of a ship like the *Sephora.* I had no doubt of it in my mind.

"Not at all the style of man. You understand," he insisted, superfluously, looking hard at me.

I smiled urbanely. He seemed at a loss for a while.

"I suppose I must report a suicide."

"Beg pardon?"

"Sui-cide! That's what I'll have to write to my owners directly I get in."

"Unless you manage to recover him before to-morrow," I assented, dispassionately. . . . "I mean, alive."

He mumbled something which I really did not catch, and I turned my ear to him in a puzzled manner. He fairly bawled:

"The land—I say, the mainland is at least seven miles off my anchorage."

"About that."

My lack of excitement, of curiosity, of surprise, of any sort of pronounced interest, began to arouse his distrust. But except for the felicitous pretence of deafness I had not tried to pretend anything. I had felt utterly incapable of playing the part of ignorance properly, and therefore was afraid to try. It is also certain that he had brought some ready-made suspicions with him, and that he viewed my politeness as a strange and unnatural phenomenon. And yet how else could I have received him? Not heartily! That was impossible for psychological reasons, which I need not state here. My only object was to keep off his inquiries. Surlily? Yes, but surliness might have provoked a point-blank question. From its novelty to him and from its nature, punctilious courtesy was the manner best calculated to restrain the man. But there was the danger of his breaking through my defence bluntly. I could not, I think, have met him by a direct lie, also for psychological (not moral) reasons. If he had only known how afraid I was of his putting my feeling of identity with the other to the test! But, strangely enough— (I thought of it only afterwards)—I believe that he was not a little disconcerted by the reverse side of that weird situation, by something in me that reminded him of the man he was seeking—suggested a mysterious similitude to the young fellow he had distrusted and disliked from the first.

However that might have been, the silence was not very prolonged. He took another oblique step.

"I reckon I had no more than a two-mile pull to your ship. Not a bit more."

'And quite enough, too, in this awful heat," I said.

Another pause full of mistrust followed. Necessity, they say, is mother of invention, but fear, too, is not barren of ingenious suggestions. And I was afraid he would ask me point-blank for news of my other self.

"Nice little saloon, isn't it?" I remarked, as if noticing for the first time the way his eyes roamed from one closed door to the other. "And very well fitted out, too. Here, for instance," I continued, reaching over the back of my seat negligently and flinging the door open, "is my bath-room."

He made an eager movement, but hardly gave it a glance. I got up, shut the door of the bath-room, and invited him to have a look round, as if I were very proud of my accommodation. He had to rise and be shown round, but he went through the business without any raptures whatever.

"And now we'll have a look at my stateroom," I declared, in a voice as loud as I dared to make it, crossing the cabin to the starboard side with purposely heavy steps.

He followed me in and gazed around. My intelligent double had vanished. I played my part.

"Very convenient—isn't it?"

"Very nice. Very comf . . ." He didn't finish and went out brusquely as if to escape from some unrighteous wiles of mine. But it was not to be. I had been too frightened not to feel vengeful; I felt I had him on the run, and I meant to keep him on the run. My polite insistence must have had something menacing in it, because he gave in suddenly. And I did not let him off a single item; mate's room, pantry, storerooms, the very sail-locker which was also under the poop—he had to look into them all. When at last I showed him out on the quarter-deck he drew a long, spiritless sigh, and mumbled dismally that he must really be going back to his ship now. I desired my mate, who had joined us, to see to the captain's boat.

The man of whiskers gave a blast on the whistle which he used to wear hanging round his neck, and yelled, "*Sephora's* away!" My double down there in my cabin must have heard, and certainly could not feel more relieved than I. Four fellows came running out from somewhere forward and went over the side, while my own men, appearing on deck too, lined the rail. I escorted my visitor to the gangway ceremoniously, and nearly overdid it. He was a tenacious beast. On the very ladder he lingered, and in that unique, guiltily conscientious manner of sticking to the point:

"I say . . . you . . . you don't think that——"

I covered his voice loudly:

"Certainly not. . . . I am delighted. Good-bye."

I had an idea of what he meant to say, and just saved myself by the privilege of defective hearing. He was too shaken generally to insist, but my mate, close witness of that parting, looked mystified and his face took on a thoughtful cast. As I did not want to appear as if I wished to avoid all communication with my officers, he had the opportunity to address me.

"Seems a very nice man. His boat's crew told our chaps a very extraordinary story, if what I am told by the steward is true. I suppose you had it from the captain, sir?"

"Yes. I had a story from the captain."

"A very horrible affair—isn't it, sir?"

"It is."

"Beats all these tales we hear about murders in Yankee ships."

"I don't think it beats them. I don't think it resembles them in the least."

"Bless my soul—you don't say so! But of course I've no acquaintance whatever with American ships, not I, so I couldn't go against your knowledge. It's horrible enough for me. . . . But the queerest part is that those fellows seemed to have some idea the man was hidden aboard here. They had really. Did you ever hear of such a thing?"

"Preposterous—isn't it?"

We were walking to and fro athwart the quarter-deck. No one of the crew forward could be seen (the day was Sunday), and the mate pursued:

"There was some little dispute about it. Our chaps took offence. 'As if we would harbour a thing like that,' they said. 'Wouldn't you like to look for him in our coal-hole?' Quite a tiff. But they made it up in the end. I suppose he did drown himself. Don't you, sir?"

"I don't suppose anything."

"You have no doubt in the matter, sir?"

"None whatever."

I left him suddenly. I felt I was producing a bad impression, but with my double down there it was most trying to be on deck. And it was almost as trying to be below. Altogether a nerve-trying situation. But on the whole I felt less torn in two when I was with him. There was no one in the whole ship whom I dared take into my confidence. Since the hands had got to know his story, it would have been impossible to pass him off for any one else, and an accidental discovery was to be dreaded now more than ever....

The steward being engaged in laying the table for dinner, we could talk only with our eyes when I first went down. Later in the afternoon we had a cautious try at whispering. The Sunday quietness of the ship was against us; the stillness of air and water around her was against us; the elements, the men were against us—everything was against us in our secret partnership; time itself—for this could not go on forever. The very trust in Providence was, I suppose, denied to his guilt. Shall I confess that this thought cast me down very much? And as to the chapter of accidents which counts for so much in the book of success, I could only hope that it was closed. For what favourable accident could be expected?

"Did you hear everything?" were my first words as soon as we took up our position side by side, leaning over my bed-place.

He had. And the proof of it was his earnest whisper, "The man told you he hardly dared to give the order."

I understood the reference to be to that saving foresail.

"Yes. He was afraid of it being lost in the setting."

"I assure you he never gave the order. He may think he did, but he never gave it. He stood there with me on the break of the poop after the maintopsail blew away, and whimpered about our last hope—positively whimpered about it and nothing else—and the night coming on! To hear one's skipper go on like that in such weather was enough to drive any fellow out of his mind. It worked me up into a sort of desperation. I just took it into my own hands and went away from him, boiling, and—— But what's the use telling you? *You* know! . . . Do you think that if I had not been pretty fierce with them I should have got the men to do anything? Not it! The bo's'n perhaps? Perhaps! It wasn't a heavy sea—it was a sea gone mad! I suppose the end of the world will be something like that; and a man may have the heart to see it coming once and be done with it—but to have to face it day after day—— I don't blame anybody. I was precious little better than the rest. Only—I was an officer of that old coal-wagon, anyhow——"

"I quite understand," I conveyed that sincere assurance into his ear. He was out of breath with whispering; I could hear him pant slightly. It was all very simple. The same strung-up force which had given twenty-four men a chance, at least, for their lives, had, in a sort of recoil, crushed an unworthy mutinous existence.

But I had no leisure to weigh the merits of the matter—footsteps in the saloon, a heavy knock. "There's enough wind to get under way with, sir." Here was the call of a new claim upon my thoughts and even upon my feelings.

"Turn the hands up," I cried through the door. "I'll be on deck directly."

I was going out to make the acquaintance of my ship. Before I left the cabin our eyes met—the eyes of the only two strangers on board. I pointed to the recessed part where the little camp-stool awaited him and laid my finger on my lips. He made a gesture—somewhat vague—a little mysterious, accompanied by a faint smile, as if of regret.

This is not the place to enlarge upon the sensations of a man who feels for the first time a ship move under his feet to his own independent word. In my case they were not unalloyed. I was not wholly alone with my command; for there was that stranger in my cabin. Or rather, I was not completely and wholly with her. Part of me was absent. That mental feeling of being in two places at once affected me physically as if the mood of secrecy had penetrated my very soul. Before an hour had elapsed since the ship had begun to move, having occasion to ask the mate (he stood by my side) to take a compass bearing of the Pagoda, I caught myself reaching up to his ear in whispers. I say I caught myself, but enough had escaped to startle the man. I can't describe it otherwise than by saying that he shied. A grave, preoccupied manner, as though he were in possession of some perplexing intelligence, did not leave him henceforth. A little later I moved away from the rail to look at the compass with such a stealthy gait that the helmsman noticed it—and I could not help noticing the unusual roundness of his eyes. These are trifling instances, though it's to no commander's advantage to be suspected of ludicrous eccentricities. But I was also more seriously affected. There are to a seaman certain words, gestures, that should in given conditions come as naturally, as instinctively as the winking of a menaced eye. A certain order should spring on to his lips without thinking; a certain sign should get itself made, so to speak, without reflection. But all unconscious alertness had abandoned me. I had to make an effort of will to recall myself back (from the cabin) to the conditions of the moment. I felt that I was appearing an irresolute commander to those people who were watching me more or less critically.

And, besides, there were the scares. On the second day out, for instance, coming off the deck in the afternoon (I had straw slippers on my bare feet) I stopped at the open pantry door and spoke to the steward. He was doing something there with his back to me. At the sound of my voice he nearly jumped out of his skin, as the saying is, and incidentally broke a cup.

"What on earth's the matter with you?" I asked, astonished.

He was extremely confused. "Beg your pardon, sir. I made sure you were in your cabin."

"You see I wasn't."

"No, sir. I could have sworn I had heard you moving in there not a moment ago. It's most extraordinary . . . very sorry, sir."

I passed on with an inward shudder. I was so identified with my secret double that I did not even mention the fact in those scanty, fearful whispers we exchanged. I suppose he had made some slight noise of some kind or other. It would have been miraculous if he hadn't at one time or another. And yet, haggard as he appeared, he looked always perfectly self-controlled, more than calm—almost invulnerable. On my suggestion he remained almost entirely in the bath-room, which, upon the whole, was the safest place. There could be really no shadow of an excuse for any one ever wanting to go in there, once the steward had done with it. It was a very tiny place. Sometimes he reclined on the floor, his legs bent, his head sustained on one elbow. At others I would find him on the camp-stool, sitting in his grey sleeping-suit and with his cropped dark hair like a patient, unmoved convict. At night I would smuggle him into my bed-place, and we would whisper together, with the regular footfalls of the officer of the watch passing and repassing over our heads. It was an infinitely miserable time. It was lucky that some tins of fine preserves were stowed in a locker in my stateroom; hard bread I could always get hold of; and so he lived on stewed chicken, paté de foie gras, asparagus, cooked oysters, sardines—on all sorts of abominable sham delicacies out of tins. My early morning coffee he always drank; and it was all I dared do for him in that respect.

Every day there was the horrible manœvering to go through so that my room and then the bath-room should be done in the usual way. I came to hate the sight of the steward, to abhor the voice of that harmless man. I felt that it was he who would bring on the disaster of discovery. It hung like a sword over our heads.

The fourth day out, I think (we were then working down the east side of the Gulf of Siam, tack for tack, in light winds and smooth water)—the fourth day, I say, of this miserable juggling with the unavoidable, as we sat at our evening meal, that man, whose slightest movement I dreaded, after putting down the dishes ran up on deck busily. This could not be dangerous. Presently he came down again; and then it appeared that he had remembered a coat of mine which I had thrown over a rail to dry after having been wetted in a shower which had passed over the ship in the afternoon. Sitting stolidly at the head of the table I became terrified at the sight of the garment on his arm. Of course he made for my door. There was no time to lose.

"Steward," I thundered. My nerves were so shaken that I could not govern my voice and conceal my agitation. This was the sort of thing that made my terrifically whiskered mate tap his forehead with his forefinger. I had detected him using that gesture while talking on deck with a confidential air to the carpenter. It was too far to hear a word, but I had no doubt that this pantomime could only refer to the strange new captain.

"Yes, sir," the pale-faced steward turned resignedly to me. It was this maddening course of being shouted at, checked without rhyme or reason, arbitrarily chased out of my cabin, suddenly called into it, sent flying out of his pantry on incomprehensible errands, that accounted for the growing wretchedness of his expression.

"Where are you going with that coat?"

"To your room, sir."

"Is there another shower coming?"

"I'm sure I don't know, sir. Shall I go up again and see, sir?"

"No! never mind."

My object was attained, as of course my other self in there would have heard everything that passed. During this interlude my two officers never raised their eyes off their respective plates; but the lip of that confounded cub, the second mate, quivered visibly.

I expected the steward to hook my coat on and come out at once. He was very slow about it; but I dominated my nervousness sufficiently not to shout after him. Suddenly I became aware (it could be heard plainly enough) that the fellow for some reason or other was opening the door of the bath-room. It was the end. The place was literally not big enough to swing a cat in. My voice died in my throat and I went stony all over. I expected to hear a yell of surprise and terror, and made a movement, but had not the strength to get on my legs. Everything remained still. Had my second self taken the poor wretch by the throat? I don't know what I could have done next moment if I had not seen the steward come out of my room, close the door, and then stand quietly by the sideboard.

"Saved," I thought. "But, no! Lost! Gone! He was gone!"

I laid my knife and fork down and leaned back in my chair.

My head swam. After a while, when sufficiently recovered to
speak in a steady voice, I instructed my mate to put the ship
round at eight o'clock himself.

"I won't come on deck," I went on. "I think I'll turn in, and
unless the wind shifts I don't want to be disturbed before midnight. I feel a bit seedy."

"You did look middling bad a little while ago," the chief
mate remarked without showing any great concern.

They both went out, and I stared at the steward clearing the
table. There was nothing to be read on that wretched man's
face. But why did he avoid my eyes I asked myself. Then I
thought I should like to hear the sound of his voice.

"Steward!"

"Sir!" Startled as usual.

"Where did you hang up that coat?"

"In the bath-room, sir." The usual anxious tone. "It's not
quite dry yet, sir."

For some time longer I sat in the cuddy. Had my double vanished as he had come? But of his coming there was an explanation, whereas his disappearance would be inexplicable. . . . I
went slowly into my dark room, shut the door, lighted the lamp,
and for a time dared not turn round. When at last I did I saw
him standing bolt-upright in the narrow recessed part. It would
not be true to say I had a shock, but an irresistible doubt of his
bodily existence flitted through my mind. Can it be, I asked myself, that he is not visible to other eyes than mine? It was like
being haunted. Motionless, with a grave face, he raised his
hands slightly at me in a gesture which meant clearly, "Heavens!
what a narrow escape!" Narrow indeed. I think I had come
creeping quietly as near insanity as any man who has not actually gone over the border. That gesture restrained me, so to
speak.

The mate with the terrific whiskers was now putting the ship
on the other tack. In the moment of profound silence which
follows upon the hands going to their stations I heard on the
poop his raised voice: "Hard alee!" and the distant shout of
the order repeated on the maindeck. The sails, in that light
breeze, made but a faint fluttering noise. It ceased. The ship
was coming round slowly; I held my breath in the renewed still-

ness of expectation; one wouldn't have thought that there was a single living soul on her decks. A sudden brisk shout, "Main-sail haul!" broke the spell, and in the noisy cries and rush overhead of the men running away with the main-brace we two, down in my cabin, came together in our usual position by the bed-place.

He did not wait for my question. "I heard him fumbling here and just managed to squat myself down in the bath," he whispered to me. "The fellow only opened the door and put his arm in to hang the coat up. All the same——"

"I never thought of that," I whispered back, even more appalled than before at the closeness of the shave, and marvelling at that something unyielding in his character which was carrying him through so finely. There was no agitation in his whisper. Whoever was being driven distracted, it was not he. He was sane. And the proof of his sanity was continued when he took up the whispering again.

"It would never do for me to come to life again."

It was something that a ghost might have said. But what he was alluding to was his old captain's reluctant admission of the theory of suicide. It would obviously serve his turn—if I had understood at all the view which seemed to govern the unalterable purpose of his action.

"You must maroon me as soon as ever you can get amongst these islands off the Cambodge shore," he went on.

"Maroon you! We are not living in a boy's adventure tale," I protested. His scornful whispering took me up.

"We aren't indeed! There's nothing of a boy's tale in this. But there's nothing else for it. I want no more. You don't suppose I am afraid of what can be done to me? Prison or gallows or whatever they may please. But you don't see me coming back to explain such things to an old fellow in a wig and twelve respectable tradesmen, do you? What can they know whether I am guilty or not—or of *what* I am guilty, either? That's my affair. What does the Bible say? 'Driven off the face of the earth.' Very well. I am off the face of the earth now. As I came at night so I shall go."

"Impossible!" I murmured. "You can't."

"Can't? . . . Not naked like a soul on the Day of Judgment.

I shall freeze on to this sleeping-suit. The Last Day is not yet—
and . . . you have understood thoroughly. Didn't you?"

I felt suddenly ashamed of myself. I may say truly that I understood—and my hesitation in letting that man swim away from
my ship's side had been a mere sham sentiment, a sort of cowardice.

"It can't be done now till next night," I breathed out. "The
ship is on the off-shore tack and the wind may fail us."

"As long as I know that you understand," he whispered. "But
of course you do. It's a great satisfaction to have got somebody
to understand. You seem to have been there on purpose." And
in the same whisper, as if we two whenever we talked had to say
things to each other which were not fit for the world to hear,
he added, "It's very wonderful."

We remained side by side talking in our secret way—but sometimes silent or just exchanging a whispered word or two at long
intervals. And as usual he stared through the port. A breath of
wind came now and again into our faces. The ship might have
been moored in dock, so gently and on an even keel she slipped
through the water, that did not murmur even at our passage,
shadowy and silent like a phantom sea.

At midnight I went on deck, and to my mate's great surprise
put the ship round on the other tack. His terrible whiskers
flitted round me in silent criticism. I certainly should not have
done it if it had been only a question of getting out of that
sleepy gulf as quickly as possible. I believe he told the second
mate, who relieved him, that it was a great want of judgment.
The other only yawned. That intolerable cub shuffled about so
sleepily and lolled against the rails in such a slack, improper
fashion that I came down on him sharply.

"Aren't you properly awake yet?"

"Yes, sir! I am awake."

"Well, then, be good enough to hold yourself as if you were.
And keep a look-out. If there's any current we'll be closing with
some islands before daylight."

The east side of the gulf is fringed with islands, some solitary,
others in groups. On the blue background of the high coast they
seem to float on silvery patches of calm water, arid and grey, or

dark green and rounded like clumps of evergreen bushes, with the larger ones, a mile or two long, showing the outlines of ridges, ribs of grey rock under the dank mantle of matted leafage. Unknown to trade, to travel, almost to geography, the manner of life they harbour is an unsolved secret. There must be villages—settlements of fishermen at least—on the largest of them, and some communication with the world is probably kept up by native craft. But all that forenoon, as we headed for them, fanned along by the faintest of breezes, I saw no sign of man or canoe in the field of the telescope I kept on pointing at the scattered group.

At noon I gave no orders for a change of course, and the mate's whiskers became much concerned and seemed to be offering themselves unduly to my notice. At last I said:

"I am going to stand right in. Quite in—as far as I can take her."

The stare of extreme surprise imparted an air of ferocity also to his eyes, and he looked truly terrific for a moment.

"We're not doing well in the middle of the gulf," I continued, casually. "I am going to look for the land breezes to-night."

"Bless my soul! Do you mean, sir, in the dark amongst the lot of all them islands and reefs and shoals?"

"Well—if there are any regular land breezes at all on this coast one must get close inshore to find them, mustn't one?"

"Bless my soul!" he exclaimed again under his breath. All that afternoon he wore a dreamy, contemplative appearance which in him was a mark of perplexity. After dinner I went into my stateroom as if I meant to take some rest. There we two bent our dark heads over a half-unrolled chart lying on my bed.

"There," I said. "It's got to be Koh-ring. I've been looking at it ever since sunrise. It has got two hills and a low point. It must be inhabited. And on the coast opposite there is what looks like the mouth of a biggish river—with some town, no doubt, not far up. It's the best chance for you that I can see."

"Anything. Koh-ring let it be."

He looked thoughtfully at the chart as if surveying chances and distances from a lofty height—and following with his eyes his own figure wandering on the blank land of Cochin-China, and then passing off that piece of paper clean out of sight into uncharted regions. And it was as if the ship had two captains to plan her course for her. I had been so worried and restless running up and down that I had not had the patience to dress that day. I had remained in my sleeping-suit, with straw slippers and a soft floppy hat. The closeness of the heat in the gulf had been most oppressive, and the crew were used to see me wandering in that airy attire.

"She will clear the south point as she heads now," I whispered into his ear. "Goodness only knows when, though, but certainly after dark. I'll edge her in to half a mile, as far as I may be able to judge in the dark——"

"Be careful," he murmured, warningly—and I realised suddenly that all my future, the only future for which I was fit, would perhaps go irretrievably to pieces in any mishap to my first command.

I could not stop a moment longer in the room. I motioned him to get out of sight and made my way on the poop. That unplayful cub had the watch. I walked up and down for a while thinking things out, then beckoned him over.

"Send a couple of hands to open the two quarter-deck ports," I said, mildly.

He actually had the impudence, or else so forgot himself in his wonder at such an incomprehensible order, as to repeat:

"Open the quarter-deck ports! What for, sir?"

"The only reason you need concern yourself about is because I tell you to do so. Have them opened wide and fastened properly."

He reddened and went off, but I believe made some jeering remark to the carpenter as to the sensible practice of ventilating a ship's quarter-deck. I know he popped into the mate's cabin to impart the fact to him because the whiskers came on deck, as it were by chance, and stole glances at me from below— for signs of lunacy or drunkenness, I suppose.

A little before supper, feeling more restless than ever, I rejoined, for a moment, my second self. And to find him sitting so quietly was surprising, like something against nature, inhuman.

I developed my plan in a hurried whisper.

"I shall stand in as close as I dare and then put her round.

I will presently find means to smuggle you out of here into the sail-locker, which communicates with the lobby. But there is an opening, a sort of square for hauling the sails out, which gives straight on the quarter-deck and which is never closed in fine weather, so as to give air to the sails. When the ship's way is deadened in stays and all the hands are aft at the main-braces you will have a clear road to slip out and get overboard through the open quarter-deck port. I've had them both fastened up. Use a rope's end to lower yourself into the water so as to avoid a splash—you know. It could be heard and cause some beastly complication."

He kept silent for a while, then whispered, "I understand."

"I won't be there to see you go," I began with an effort. "The rest . . . I only hope I have understood, too."

"You have. From first to last"—and for the first time there seemed to be a faltering, something strained in his whisper. He caught hold of my arm, but the ringing of the supper bell made me start. He didn't, though; he only released his grip.

After supper I didn't come below again till well past eight o'clock. The faint, steady breeze was loaded with dew; and the wet, darkened sails held all there was of propelling power in it. The night, clear and starry, sparkled darkly, and the opaque, lightless patches shifting slowly against the low stars were the drifting islets. On the port bow there was a big one more distant and shadowily imposing by the great space of sky it eclipsed.

On opening the door I had a back view of my very own self looking at a chart. He had come out of the recess and was standing near the table.

"Quite dark enough," I whispered.

He stepped back and leaned against my bed with a level, quiet glance. I sat on the couch. We had nothing to say to each other. Over our heads the officer of the watch moved here and there. Then I heard him move quickly. I knew what that meant. He was making for the companion; and presently his voice was outside my door.

"We are drawing in pretty fast, sir. Land looks rather close."

"Very well," I answered. "I am coming on deck directly."

I waited till he was gone out of the cuddy, then rose. My double moved too. The time had come to exchange our last whispers, for neither of us was ever to hear each other's natural voice.

"Look here!" I opened a drawer and took out three sovereigns. "Take this anyhow. I've got six and I'd give you the lot, only I must keep a little money to buy some fruit and vegetables for the crew from native boats as we go through Sunda Straits."

He shook his head.

"Take it," I urged him, whispering desperately. "No one can tell what——"

He smiled and slapped meaningly the only pocket of the sleeping-jacket. It was not safe, certainly. But I produced a large old silk handkerchief of mine, and tying the three pieces of gold in a corner, pressed it on him. He was touched, I suppose, because he took it at last and tied it quickly round his waist under the jacket, on his bare skin.

Our eyes met; several seconds elapsed, till, our glances still mingled, I extended my hand and turned the lamp out. Then I passed through the cuddy, leaving the door of my room wide open. . . . "Steward!"

He was still lingering in the pantry in the greatness of his zeal, giving a rub-up to a plated cruet stand the last thing before going to bed. Being careful not to wake up the mate, whose room was opposite, I spoke in an undertone.

He looked round anxiously. "Sir!"

"Can you get me a little hot water from the galley?"

"I am afraid, sir, the galley fire's been out for some time now."

"Go and see."

He flew up the stairs.

"Now," I whispered, loudly, into the saloon—too loudly, perhaps, but I was afraid I couldn't make a sound. He was by my side in an instant—the double captain slipped past the stairs—through a tiny dark passage . . . a sliding door. We were in the sail-locker, scrambling on our knees over the sails. A sudden thought struck me. I saw myself wandering barefooted, bareheaded, the sun beating on my dark poll. I snatched off my floppy hat and tried hurriedly in the dark to ram it on my other self. He dodged and fended off silently. I wonder what he thought had come to me before he understood and suddenly desisted. Our hands met gropingly, lingered united in a steady, motionless clasp for a second. . . . No word was breathed by either of us when they separated.

I was standing quietly by the pantry door when the steward returned.

"Sorry, sir. Kettle barely warm. Shall I light the spirit-lamp?"

"Never mind."

I came out on deck slowly. It was now a matter of conscience to shave the land as close as possible—for now he must go overboard whenever the ship was put in stays. Must! There could be no going back for him. After a moment I walked over to leeward and my heart flew into my mouth at the nearness of the land on the bow. Under any other circumstances I would not have held on a minute longer. The second mate had followed me anxiously.

I looked on till I felt I could command my voice.

"She will weather," I said then in a quiet tone.

"Are you going to try that, sir?" he stammered out incredulously.

I took no notice of him and raised my tone just enough to be heard by the helmsman.

"Keep her good full."

"Good full, sir."

The wind fanned my cheek, the sails slept, the world was silent. The strain of watching the dark loom of the land grow bigger and denser was too much for me. I had shut my eyes—because the ship must go closer. She must! The stillness was intolerable. Were we standing still?

When I opened my eyes the second view started my heart with a thump. The black southern hill of Koh-ring seemed to hang right over the ship like a towering fragment of the everlasting night. On that enormous mass of blackness there was not a gleam to be seen, not a sound to be heard. It was gliding irresistibly towards us and yet seemed already within reach of the hand. I saw the vague figures of the watch grouped in the waist, gazing in awed silence.

"Are you going on, sir?" inquired an unsteady voice at my elbow.

I ignored it. I had to go on.

"Keep her full. Don't check her way. That won't do now," I said, warningly.

"I can't see the sails very well," the helmsman answered me, in strange, quavering tones.

Was she close enough? Already she was, I won't say in the shadow of the land, but in the very blackness of it, already swallowed up as it were, gone too close to be recalled, gone from me altogether.

"Give the mate a call," I said to the young man who stood at my elbow as still as death. "And turn all hands up."

My tone had a borrowed loudness reverberated from the height of the land. Several voices cried out together: "We are all on deck, sir."

Then stillness again, with the great shadow gliding closer, towering higher, without a light, without a sound. Such a hush had fallen on the ship that she might have been a bark of the dead floating in slowly under the very gate of Erebus.

"My God! Where are we?"

It was the mate moaning at my elbow. He was thunderstruck, and as it were deprived of the moral support of his whiskers. He clapped his hands and absolutely cried out, "Lost!"

"Be quiet," I said, sternly.

He lowered his tone, but I saw the shadowy gesture of his despair. "What are we doing here?"

"Looking for the land wind."

He made as if to tear his hair, and addressed me recklessly.

"She will never get out. You have done it, sir. I knew it'd end in something like this. She will never weather, and you are too close now to stay. She'll drift ashore before she's round. O my God!"

I caught his arm as he was raising it to batter his poor devoted head, and shook it violently.

"She's ashore already," he wailed, trying to tear himself away.

"Is she? . . . Keep good full there!"

"Good full, sir," cried the helmsman in a frightened, thin, child-like voice.

I hadn't let go the mate's arm and went on shaking it. "Ready about, do you hear? You go forward"—shake—"and stop there"—shake—"and hold your noise"—shake——"and see these head-sheets properly overhauled"—shake, shake—shake.

And all the time I dared not look towards the land lest my heart should fail me. I released my grip at last and he ran forward as if fleeing for dear life.

I wondered what my double there in the sail-locker thought of this commotion. He was able to hear everything—and perhaps he was able to understand why, on my conscience, it had to be thus close—no less. My first order "Hard alee!" re-echoed ominously under the towering shadow of Koh-ring as if I had shouted in a mountain gorge. And then I watched the land intently. In that smooth water and light wind it was impossible to feel the ship coming-to. No! I could not feel her. And my second self was making now ready to slip out and lower himself overboard. Perhaps he was gone already . . . ?

The great black mass brooding over our very mastheads began to pivot away from the ship's side silently. And now I forgot the secret stranger ready to depart, and remembered only that I was a total stranger to the ship. I did not know her. Would she do it? How was she to be handled?

I swung the mainyard and waited helplessly. She was perhaps stopped, and her very fate hung in the balance, with the black mass of Koh-ring like the gate of the everlasting night towering over her taffrail. What would she do now? Had she way on her yet? I stepped to the side swiftly, and on the shadowy water I could see nothing except a faint phosphorescent flash revealing the glassy smoothness of the sleeping surface. It was impossible to tell—and I had not learned yet the feel of my ship. Was she moving? What I needed was something easily seen, a piece of paper, which I could throw overboard and watch. I had nothing on me. To run down for it I didn't dare. There was no time. All at once my strained, yearning stare distinguished a white object floating within a yard of the ship's side. White on the black water. A phosphorescent flash passed under it. What was that thing? . . . I recognised my own floppy hat. It must have fallen off his head . . . and he didn't bother. Now I had what I wanted—the saving mark for my eyes. But I hardly thought of my other self, now gone from the ship, to be hidden for ever from all friendly faces, to be a fugitive and a vagabond on the earth, with no brand of the curse on his sane forehead to stay a slaying hand . . . too proud to explain.

And I watched the hat—the expression of my sudden pity for his mere flesh. It had been meant to save his homeless head from the dangers of the sun. And now—behold—it was saving the ship, by serving me for a mark to help out the ignorance of my strangeness. Ha! It was drifting forward, warning me just in time that the ship had gathered sternway.

"Shift the helm," I said in a low voice to the seaman standing still like a statue.

The man's eyes glistened wildly in the binnacle light as he jumped round to the other side and spun round the wheel.

I walked to the break of the poop. On the overshadowed deck all hands stood by the forebraces waiting for my order. The stars ahead seemed to be gliding from right to left. And all was so still in the world that I heard the quiet remark, "She's round," passed in a tone of intense relief between two seamen.

"Let go and haul."

The foreyards ran round with a great noise, amidst cheery cries. And now the frightful whiskers made themselves heard giving various orders. Already the ship was drawing ahead. And I was alone with her. Nothing! no one in the world should stand now between us, throwing a shadow on the way of silent knowledge and mute affection, the perfect communion of a seaman with his first command.

Walking to the taffrail, I was in time to make out, on the very edge of a darkness thrown by a towering black mass like the very gateway of Erebus—yes, I was in time to catch an evanescent glimpse of my white hat left behind to mark the spot where the secret sharer of my cabin and of my thoughts, as though he were my second self, had lowered himself into the water to take his punishment: a free man, a proud swimmer striking out for a new destiny.

Echo Structures: Conrad's
The Secret Sharer

LOUIS H. LEITER

I know exactly what I am doing. *Mr. George Blackwood's incidental remark in his last letter that the story is not fairly begun yet is in a measure correct but, on a large view, beside the point. For, the writing is as good as I can make it (first duty), and in the light of the final incident,* the whole story in all its descriptive detail shall fall into its place—*acquire its value and its significance.* This is my method based on deliberate conviction. *I've never departed from it. I call your own kind self to witness and I beg to instance Karain*—Lord Jim *(where the method is fully developed)—the last pages of* Heart of Darkness *where the interview of the man and the girl locks in—as it were—the whole 30,000 words of narrative description into one suggestive view of a whole phase of life, and makes of that story something quite on another plane than an anecdote of a man who went mad in the Centre of Africa. And* Youth *itself . . . exists only in virtue of my fidelity to the idea and the method. The favourable critics of that story . . . remarked with a sort of surprise "This after all is a story for boys yet—"*
Exactly. Out of the material of a boy's story I've made Youth *by the force of the idea expressed in accordance with a strict conception of my method. And however unfavourably it may affect the business in hand I must confess that I shall not depart from my method. I am at need prepared to explain on what grounds I think it a true method. All my endeavours*

185

*shall be directed to understand it better, to develop its great
possibilities, to acquire greater skill in the handling—to
mastery in short.*

(Joseph Conrad's letter to William Blackwood, 31 May 1902,
concerning *Heart of Darkness*)

For the most part critics agree that the narrator of Joseph Conrad's *The Secret Sharer* is a double for the protagonist, that actions and gestures of this newly appointed captain are reflected
in the movements and behavior of the recently escaped Leggatt,
and that each man echoes the most private thoughts and sentiments of the other. A series of echoes established by means of
image, metaphor, symbol, and mime consistently suggest to the
reader the manner in which he should interpret the roles of
Leggatt and the captain-narrator. Although they are one person
figuratively, the inner and the outer, the unconscious and the
conscious, they are split for didactic and aesthetic reasons into
two characters. What has escaped notice, however, is that echo
structures similar to those which portray character have been
employed for other reasons as well as this throughout the short
novel. Structures not only of character but also of narrative action, parable, metaphor, and the like, become a fundamental
means for achieving aesthetic and thematic effects.[1]

The echo structure: An echo structure implies one or more
structures similar to itself. The tautology which is the echo
structure may be a repeated symbol, metaphor, scene, pattern of
action, state of being, myth, fable, or archetype. If viewed within
the perspective of Biblical story or classical myth, either directly
stated in the text of the story or implied, that perspective may

[1] All quotations are from *'Twixt Land and Sea* by Joseph Conrad, 1912,
Doubleday & Company, Inc. For the most perceptive analyses of *The Secret
Sharer* I refer the reader to R. B. West and R. W. Stallman, *The Art of Modern
Fiction* (New York, 1949) , pp. 490-500; Albert J. Guerard's introduction to
Heart of Darkness and The Secret Sharer (New York, 1950) , pp. 7-15; Winifred
Lynskey's provocative questions and statements in *Reading Modern Fiction*
(New York, 1952) , pp. 147-149. All italics are mine except the title of the novel
and the name of the ship.

I am grateful to Robert Creed and George Monteiro of Brown University
for their encouragement and criticism.

suffuse the echo structures of similar construction with additional meanings. If seen from the vantage of imagery alone, an echo structure is what has been called the principle of reflexive reference.[2] It evokes thematic meaning when the total pattern of images has been examined in the context in which it appears. The thematic significance of echo structures will be demonstrated in the course of this essay.

Image cluster as echo structure: In this essay an image is any word which creates a relatively concrete "picture" in or presents some configuration to the reader's mind. Almost any word may be used for this purpose. Clusters of images occur when certain groups of words fall together recurrently so that we identify them as somehow significantly related. Thus Conrad's short novel opens with these lines:

> On my right hand there were *lines of fishing-stakes* resembling *a mysterious system* of *half-submerged bamboo fences, incomprehensible* in its division of the domain of tropical fishes, and *crazy of aspect* as if abandoned for ever by some *nomad tribe of fishermen now gone to the other end of the ocean*; for there was no sign of human habitation as far as the eye could reach.

In isolation these opening lines accomplish little more than the establishing of an appropriate atmosphere of mystery and the underlining of the narrator-captain's solitude as a stranger to his ship, to his men, and to himself. A few hours later, however, as the narrator paces the deck of his first command after sending all his men to rest, he suddenly discovers the ladder hanging over the side:

> Then I reflected that I had myself peremptorily dismissed my officers from duty, and by my own act had prevented the anchor-watch being formally set and things properly attended to. . . . Not from compunction certainly, but, as it were mechanically, *I proceeded to get the ladder in myself.* Now a side-ladder of that sort is a *light affair* and comes in easily, yet my *vigorous tug,* which should have brought it flying on board, merely recoiled upon my body in *a totally unexpected jerk.* What the

[2] I am referring to Joseph Frank, "Special Form in Modern Literature," *Sewanee Review,* 53:221-240 (Summer, 1945), 53:433-456 (Autumn, 1945), 53: 643-653 (Winter, 1945).

devil! . . . I was so *astounded* by the immovableness of that ladder that I remained stock-still, trying to account for it myself *like that imbecile mate of mine*. In the end, of course, I put my head over the rail. . . . I saw at once *something elongated and pale floating very close to the ladder*. Before I could form a guess a faint flash of phosphorescent light, which seemed to issue suddenly from the naked body of a man, flickered in the sleeping water. . . . *As he hung by the ladder*, like a resting swimmer, the sea-lightning played about his limbs at every stir; and he appeared in it *ghastly, silvery, fish-like. He remained as mute as a fish, too*.

In this passage the imagery cluster of the opening lines is echoed. However the original cluster has been modified into another cluster which resembles the first one but with certain significant changes. What is described as a seascape in the first passage is echoed in the second, and we shall see it once more in a third, with a more personal significance for the narrator. The "half-submerged bamboo fences" for catching fish suggest the "ladder," that "light affair" which the narrator, annoyed with his own negligence, "proceeded to get . . . in." The "tug" and "jerk" of the second passage further suggest the idea of the narrator's fishing with something like a bamboo fence which has undergone a transformation into a ladder. "Mysterious" of the first passage echoes in "astounded" of the second, while "crazy of aspect" in the first appears as "imbecile mate" in the second. And "fishermen" of the former echoes in "fish-like" of the latter, reinforced by Leggatt's being "mute as a fish."

This first cluster of images along with the second, somewhat modified cluster appears once more in *The Secret Sharer*. Toward the end of the story when the narrator relates that he must rid himself and his ship of Leggatt, he thinks:

Whoever was being driven distracted, it was not he. He was sane. And the proof of his sanity was continued when he took up the whispering again. "It would never do for me to come to life again. . . . What does the Bible say? *'Driven off the face of the earth.'* Very well. *I am off the face of the earth now. As I came at night so I shall go.*"

Once more the cluster of images echoes in this passage. We perceive that the two earlier structures are here somewhat shortened, some elements eliminated, and others echoed more strongly in modified form. "Distracted" and "sane" and "sanity" echo one set of images, while the Biblical quotation, "Driven off the face of the earth," transforms the image of "nomad tribe" into something more mysterious and frightening.

What the second and third passages accomplish is to charge the first passage with meanings which it does not possess when first read. Only after reading the second passage, and especially after reading the third, do we see that the first is a symbolic seascape corresponding point by point to the central thematic tensions of the novel and to the narrator's lack of knowledge of his own untested psyche. What we perceive through the narrator's eyes as he describes the setting is the projected, unexplored, unknown seascape of his own mind plucked, as it were, inside out and superimposed on the sea and land; but neither the narrator nor the reader becomes fully aware of this until much later. For the reader this occurs at the moment he perceives that the imagery clusters in the two widely separated echo structures have already appeared in the introductory passage.

The setting at the beginning is mysterious, atmospherically strange and unknown. Gradual revelation of and coming to terms with self throughout the novel is accompanied by a gradual change in and transformation of the imagery clusters parallel to the awakening to self knowledge. The bamboo fence belonging to the strangers becomes the narrator's own ladder, the means by which he "hooks" and brings to the surface his own secret self, that strange being who seems to live beyond the pale of human laws and who does indeed circumvent human punishment. The imagery in "fishing-stakes . . . crazy of aspect" echoes in the narrator's being "astounded" when he pulls at the ladder with the creature, "mute as a fish," at its end, and in his description of his Chief Mate as an "imbecile." What this identification by means of imagery suggests is that somehow the three men, Leggatt-narrator-mate, are one person, or that certain aspects of their personalities are to be identified as similar.

Leggatt performs the role of the narrator's inner self, the possibility of the defections of the unconscious mind, its lawless (libidinous) forces breaking forth and overpowering law and order. Since they are identified through the imagery cluster, however, a specific aspect of the narrator's personality must be embodied in his Chief Mate. The narrator becomes more and more certain throughout the novel that he is losing his mind, that he is insane, that perhaps he is only imagining that he shares his cabin with Leggatt whom no one else has seen. In this way he gradually drifts toward the "imbecility" which he attaches so violently to his Chief Mate. Then in the third echo structure, the narrator confirms his own dangerous psychic condition when he seriously hints at his gradual loss of sanity, "Whoever was being driven distracted, it was not he. He was sane. And the proof of his sanity was continued when he took up the whispering again."

Conrad, I believe, wants us to see here that both men are indeed different aspects of the narrator's personality. The Chief Mate in many respects is just as dangerous as Leggatt. It is he who goes to pieces during the narrator's supreme test. Like Leggatt and like Captain Archbold of the *Sephora* he loses control of himself when in danger. Unlike Leggatt but still like Captain Archbold, the Chief Mate is obtuse. This very insensitivity, lack of trust, unawareness of the possible strength of personality, leads to his breakdown. But it also contributes to the narrator's demonstration of control over that very weakness of his own personality during the final trial scene in which he seizes the blubbering Chief Mate and transfers his strength to that man. Through this gesture (a mime repeated from the sail-locker scene where he had gripped Leggatt just before consigning him to the deep) the narrator symbolically conquers the obtuseness of his own personality. The imagery cluster identifies the three men as one person and imagistically suggests that "insanity" and "imbecility" are symbolic of weakness or obtuseness. That part of the first cluster which is not echoed in the second cluster but appears in the third cluster of images, "some nomad tribe of fishermen now gone to the other end of the ocean," suggests the fate of Leggatt and the fate of the narrator himself. The Biblical echo, "Driven off the face of the earth," is identified throughout *The Secret Sharer* with the Cain and Abel story, to which I shall return later in this essay. The first time the imagery appears, it is impersonally attached to "nomad tribe"; it does not affect the narrator in any way, although when we glance back at it we see it as part of the symbolic construction in that first passage to which "meanings" may be attached. Then suddenly a stranger, a wanderer, a swimmer really, appears at the ship's side. The absence of this part of the cluster of images in the second echo passage suggests the absence of knowledge as to who the stranger is or what he represents. But when the cluster appears again in the third echo passage, the narrator-captain has already gained knowledge of himself, of Leggatt, of his Chief Mate, and of the perilous situation on board his ship; he knows that he must help Leggatt, the Cain aspect of his personality, escape back into the sea (come to terms with or repress his inner self). The imagery cluster consequently from its introduction (nomad tribe) to its final echo (the Cain as wanderer reference) describes a movement from the superficial to the profound, from lack of knowledge of personality to penetrating awareness of what that part of the personality is capable of accomplishing—victory over moral disorder and victory over obtuseness.

Parable as echo structure: Parable, a short, simple story or observation, usually but not always an allegory, may serve as an echo structure. In the beginning of *The Secret Sharer*, as the narrator stands on the deck of his first command, watching the departing tug, which brought him to the harbor, he observes:

Here and there *gleams as of a few scattered pieces of silver* marked the windings of the great river; and on the nearest of them, just within the bar, *the tug steaming right into the land became lost to my sight, hull and funnel and masts, as though the impassive earth had swallowed her up without an effort, without a tremor.* My eye followed the light cloud of her smoke, now here, now there, above the plain, according to the devious curves of the stream, but always fainter and farther away, till *I lost it at last behind the mitre-shaped hill of the great pagoda.* And then I was left alone with my ship, anchored at the head of the Gulf of Siam.

This parable of the tug is echoed later in the novel when Conrad expands it into a major action, the most important one of the novel. As the tug steams into the land, so does the narrator's ship steam into the land when he sails in shore to rid himself of

Leggatt. The identity of the echoed structures is made clear through the use of corresponding images. The water in both passages is silvery; a tug appears in one, a ship in the other; the "mitre-shaped" hill in the first, the mountain "Koh-ring" in the second. This is strengthened in the echo structure at the moment of climax when the narrator says of his ship, "Already she was, I won't say in the shadow of the land, but in the very blackness of it, already swallowed up as it were, gone too close to be recalled, gone from me altogether." The "silver" marking the passage of the river from the land into the sea will be reversed in the final structure into the "white hat" which marked the passage of Leggatt towards the land, with a reversal of the action included in the structures "from land to sea" to "from sea to land."

The major difference between the parable and its tautological echo in the latter structure is one of expansion and substitution; the dozen lines of the parable become the half dozen pages of the dilated action. Similarly that which the twenty-seven year old narrator impassively narrates in the first structure becomes that in which he is intimately even passionately involved in the echo structure. He speaks in the parable of the land as "impassive"; but in the structure of the echoed parable, the land becomes a place of "unrest" and "disquiet." The echo suggests, consequently, not only a structural principle operative in the novel, but also the result of "involvement" in experience, an experience which the narrator, untried in his new command, has never undergone previously, one which he observes in the parable's structure and one which he suffers through most intimately in the echo structure. The echoed, symbolic parable suggests that impassivity becomes disquietude when impersonality, lack of dedication to knowledge of self, becomes conscious dedication to a course of behavior leading to self-knowledge. "I wondered how far I should turn out faithful to that ideal conception of one's own personality every man sets up for himself secretly." As such this echoed parabolic structure establishes thematic meanings.

One more example of this principle will contribute to our understanding here. When thinking of his new Chief Mate, the narrator describes him in these terms:

He was of a painstaking turn of mind. As he used to say, he "liked to account to himself" for practically everything that came in his way, down to *a miserable scorpion he had found in his cabin a week before. The why and wherefore of that scorpion—how it got on board and came to select his room rather than the pantry (which was a dark place and more what a scorpion would be partial to), and how on earth it managed to drown itself in the inkwell of his writing-desk*—had exercised him infinitely.

The extended actions of Leggatt in *The Secret Sharer* are an echo structure of the parable of the scorpion. As a matter of fact, the parable is almost a brief allegory of the entire action of the novel itself. The scorpion appears from the sea and enters the Chief Mate's cabin only to fall into the ink. Leggatt rises from the sea, enters the narrator's cabin, and then returns to the black waters of Koh-ring. Both scorpion and Leggatt are identified with light. The latter appears beside the ship all flashes of fire and phosphorescence; the former seeks the light of the Chief Mate's cabin. And Captain Archbold of the *Sephora*, repeating the allegory once more, appears over the side of the ship in daylight and disappears over her side a short time later with his red whiskers twitching.

As in the instance of the tug-ship parable, the scorpion-Leggatt parable structure is expanded into many times its former, brief form and is modified and told in human terms. The echo structure of the scorpion parable appears a fourth time when after Captain Archbold of the *Sephora* departs, the narrator's Chief Mate tells him that the crew of the *Sephora* suspected Leggatt was aboard:

"There was some little dispute about it. Our chaps took offence. *'As if we would harbour a thing like that,'* they said. *'Wouldn't you like to look for him in our coal-hole?'* Quite a tiff. But they made it up in the end. *I suppose he did drown himself. Don't you, sir?"*

Comparison of the scorpion parable and the echoing structures suggests the significance of the echo technique. Thematically the parable symbolizes something about the echoing action. The scorpion, mysterious, poisonous, inexplicable, provides meanings for Leggatt's actions, meanings for the consequences of those actions, which are not explicitly stated. Leggatt's arrival on the ship is as mysterious as that of the vermin and as dangerous to the narrator if he remains on the ship. The deadly quality of the scorpion is precisely that danger the captain experiences in his intercourse with Leggatt, the gradual but continuous poisoning of his relationship with his crew. Thus in another brief echo of the scorpion parable, Leggatt tells the narrator of the steward and second mate of the *Sephora* who hated him "like poison." And in still another the poison is at work in the narrator's ship:

I was not wholly alone with my command; for there was that stranger in my cabin. *Or rather, I was not completely and wholly with her. Part of me was absent. That mental feeling of being in two places at once affected me physically as if the mood of secrecy had penetrated my very soul.*

Drowning of the scorpion signified not only the return of Leggatt to the black waters of Koh-ring but also the metaphorical death of the captain's "secret-sharer," the inner, uncontrollable, unconscious self, which vermin like, must return into the great sea of the unconscious from which it arose.

As the consequence of the use of parable as a structure which is echoed again and again in the novel, multiple thematic and symbolic dimensions are created which contribute to total meaning.[3]

---

[3] West and Stallman in their sensitive analysis of *The Secret Sharer* suggest that the novel might be read as an allegory of the artist and his coming to terms with himself and his materials. If we accept this, then we may read the parable of the scorpion as an epitomization of the writer's situation. The mysterious and dangerous materials which rise from the sea-unconscious are symbolized by the scorpion. His entering the lighted cabin suggests a bringing into consciousness if we see the cabin as a created, ordered, civilized place, the home of the meticulous "Chief Mate." The scorpion's drowning in "ink" further suggests the transformation these forces must undergo from poison to ink, the sublimation of those forces into written form. There are also a number of provocative hints in the novel as Leggatt and the narrator pour over charts, books, and the like.

Action as echo structure: Action may also create echo structures. When Leggatt tells the young narrator of the man he has murdered, he says:

There are fellows that an angel from heaven——And I am not that. He was one of those creatures that are just simmering all the time with a silly sort of wickedness. Miserable devils that have no business to live at all. He wouldn't do his duty and wouldn't let anybody else do theirs. . . . *He gave me some of his cursed insolence at the sheet.* I tell you I was overdone with this terrific weather that seemed to have no end to it. Terrific, I tell you—and a deep ship. *I believe the fellow himself was half crazed with funk. It was no time for gentlemanly reproof, so I turned around and felled him like an ox. He up and at me. We closed just as an awful sea made for the ship.* All hands saw it coming and took to the rigging, but *I had him by the throat, and went on shaking him like a rat,* the men above us yelling, '*Look out! look out!*' Then a crash as if the sky had fallen on my head. They say that for over ten minutes *hardly anything was to be seen of the ship*—just the three masts and a bit of the forecastle head and of the poop all awash driving along in a smother of foam. It was a miracle that they found us, jammed together behind the forebits. *It's clear that I meant business, because I was holding him by the throat still when they picked us up.* He was black in the face.

Later when the narrator takes his untried ship into shore, ostensibly to catch the land breezes, the following transpires between him and his Chief Mate hard upon a description of the "very blackness" of the mountain Koh-ring:

Then stillness again, with the great shadow gliding closer, towering higher, without a light, without a sound. Such a hush had fallen on the ship that she might have been *a bark of the dead floating in slowly under the very gate of Erebus.*
"My God! Where are we?"
It was the mate moaning at my elbow. He was thunderstruck, and as it were deprived of the moral support of his whiskers. He clapped his hands and absolutely cried out, "Lost!"
"Be quiet," I said sternly.
He lowered his tone, but I saw the shadowy gesture of his despair. "What are we doing here?" . . .
He made as if to tear his hair, and addressed me recklessly.

"She will never get out. You have done it, sir. I knew it'd end in something like this. She will never weather, and you are too close now to stay. She'll drift ashore before she's round. O my God!"

I caught his arm as he was raising it to batter his poor devoted head, and shook it violently.

"She's ashore already," he wailed, trying to tear himself away.

"Is she? . . . Keep good full there!"

"Good full, sir," cried the helmsman in a frightened, thin, child-like voice.

I hadn't let go the mate's arm and went on shaking it. "Ready about, do you hear? You go forward"—shake—*"and stop there"*—shake—*"and hold your noise"*—shake—*"and see these head-sheets properly overhauled"*—shake, shake—shake.

And all the time I dared not look towards the land lest my heart should fail me. *I released my grip at last and he ran forward as if fleeing for dear life.*

The dramatic actions of the two passages are analogous: both Leggatt and the narrator, caught in perilous situations, attempt to save their ships; both have an encounter with someone who opposes their will; both come to grips with that person; both save their ships; but both face tests which they solve differently. Clearly the second of the two structural units is an echo of the former with certain very important changes. Thus in the latter structure, it is not the disobedient sailor's face which is black, that miserable devil "who had no business to live at all." That color has been transferred to the threatening land. Likewise, Conrad transfers in the echoed passage Leggatt's epithet for the recalcitrant sailor to the land, "the very gate of Erebus."

What Conrad achieves by shifting images from the sailor to the land is a transference of symbolic meaning, so that instead of the Chief Mate's being the threat, it is the land which threatens the ship and crew with evil and annihilation. To come to knowledge of self is a hellish business; the seeking of the winds of self knowledge and reconciliation with self and the world is full of terror, fraught with danger to life and soul. The new captain's Chief Mate does not resemble the murdered sailor in action as we might expect; for the land because it assumes the epithet, symbolizes cursedness, hellishness, and deadliness, the meaning also of the storm of the original passage in which Leggatt was involved in murder. In the echo structure, it is not a noisy typhoon which releases destruction; it is the silence of the ship and land and the Chief Mate's fear of the narrator's lack of experience, youth, and strange behavior, which unsettle him. Similarly, as Leggatt makes clear, the roles in the echo structure are a reversal of those of the earlier structure. Speaking to the narrator, Leggatt says of Captain Archbold during the typhoon:

I assure you he never gave the order. He may think he did, but he never gave it. *He stood there with me on the break of the poop after the main-topsail blew away, and whimpered about our last hope—positively whimpered about it and nothing else—and the night coming on! To hear one's skipper go on like that in such weather was enough to drive any fellow out of his mind.*

The meaning of the technique of the echo action in these passages is somewhat elusive but not impossible to establish. Analogous scenes suggest by means of similar images and similar miming that the two scenes are essentially the ame scene, something like archetypal initiations or tests. The first of the two scenes creates a kind of order, for good or for evil, against which the second tautological structure must be judged and evaluated. The difference between the two scenes, those dissimilarities which appear in the echo structure, when evaluated within the framework of the former scene, suggest the meaning of the latter scene. Both men, Leggatt and the young captain, undergo the same experience; Leggatt seizes the man by the throat at the climax of his archetypal trial by storm and kills him in a fit of uncontrolled passion; the narrator also seizes his Chief Mate under similar circumstances, his archetypal trial by silence, but by controlling himself, controlling the frightened, disbelieving man, he controls the ship and consequently saves her from destruction, while saving his reputation and winning the respect of his crew. The action of the echo structure implies, it seems to me, a moral judgment of Leggatt, although it does not state the judgment openly. It dramatizes it and by doing so makes the reader psychologically aware of it. At the same time the echo scene declares the moral superiority of the consciously aware narrator-captain who has come to face his secret inner self, to conquer it, and to control it.

Archetype, myth, or Biblical story as echo structure: A course of action, a metaphor, a symbol, an image, and the like, repeated often enough to assume traditional meanings and to be recognized as ritualistic is what is meant by archetype or archetypal pattern. The life and death of Christ is archetypal in these terms. It has certain similarities to the life, death, and resurrection of pagan gods. Dionysus, Tammuz, Adonis, the passing of the seasons, the rising and setting of the sun, and the phases of the moon, all recognizable as archetypes. The cross is an archetype which contains in it the entire Christian story. "Miserable devils," "hellish spell of bad weather," and "gate of Erebus" are conceivable as archetypes of the demonic in *The Secret Sharer*. Archetypes may be obvious at once if they have not undergone complex disguise, or they may be distorted, disguised, fragmentary, inverted, or merely implied.[4]

In Conrad's novel several direct references to the Cain and Abel archetype draw our attention to its relation to the Leggatt story. Leggatt describes his experience to the narrator-captain in these words:

Devil only knows what the skipper wasn't afraid of (all his nerve went to pieces altogether in that hellish spell of bad weather we had)—of what the law would do to him—of his wife, perhaps. Oh, yes! she's on board. Though I don't think she would have meddled. She would have been only too glad to have me out of the ship in any way. *The "brand of Cain" business, don't you see. That's all right. I was ready enough to go off wandering on the face of the earth—and that was price enough to pay for an Abel of that sort.*

Later the captain reminds us of the story when he thinks, "The very trust in Providence was, I suppose, denied to his guilt." And once more it is echoed when the narrator and Leggatt search the map of the Gulf of Siam for an appropriate place for Leggatt's escape:

[4] These remarks are based on Northrop Frye's *Anatomy of Criticism* (Princeton, 1957), pp. 131-239. I have attempted to extend Professor Frye's theory of archetypes in two directions, practical and aesthetic.

He looked thoughtfully at the chart as if surveying chances and distances from a lofty height—*and following with his eyes his own figure*
wandering on the blank land of Cochin-China, and then passing off that
piece of paper clean out of sight into uncharted regions."

This is re-echoed in the structure of Leggatt's word when he decides to return to the sea, "What does the Bible say? *'Driven off*
the face of the earth.' Very well. I am off the face of the earth
now. As I came at night so I shall go." The obvious references
to the Cain and Abel archetypal structure are paralleled, as Leggatt suggests, in his relationship with the murdered sailor. As
such they dictate a major structure of the novel, a ritual of
murder, guilt, judgment, banishment or escape, and wandering,
corresponding to the narrative course of Leggatt's story. But
that is not all because the brother-murder-banishment-wandering
archetypal structure echoes most of the principal relationships
in the story. Leggatt and the murdered man; the narrator and
Leggatt; the captain of the *Sephora* and Leggatt; the narrator
and his Chief Mate and crew. Although Leggatt suggests the
archetypal relationship between himself and the murdered man
and the Cain and Abel story, the archetype is not complete because the captain of the *Sephora* also becomes the Cain figure
who wants to kill Leggatt by turning him over to the law for
trial. Because he is jealous of Leggatt's having saved the ship
with the reefed sail, the *Sephora's* captain plays in an ironic reversal the Cain role to Leggatt's Abel. The Cain-Abel archetype
circumscribes the narrator-Leggatt relationship as well, the longest pattern of action and most important relationship of the
novel, for the narrator in a role comparable to that of Cain, figuratively kills his Abel-Leggatt when he consigns him to the sea.
But the meaning of this archetypal action is symbolic and thematic because this Cain recognizes that he must destroy his Abel
personality, an inversion of the Abel roll, by sending him back
to the sea. That the narrator will wander the face of the earth
like Cain is made clear in the last sentence of the novel. But by
shifting our perspective slightly, we observe that the relationship of the narrator to his Chief Mate and crew and ship is also
a fragment of the echoing Cain and Abel archetype. The nar-

rator may have killed the hysterical Chief Mate, as Leggatt killed the mutinous sailor, and as Cain killed Abel, but he does something else. By transcending and controlling the Abels on the ship, Leggatt, the Chief Mate, the crew, he avoids the Cain role and, incidentally, transforms the archetype even as he completes it.

The echoed archetypal structures suggest the multiplicity of similar experiences. They suggest that every man may be his brother's killer wittingly or unwittingly. The captain of the *Sephora,* for instance, wishes to preserve law and order by turning Leggatt over to the courts, but how much of jealousy and shame lie behind his decision he never admits. To what degree does he maintain morality and responsibility and to what degree does he demand the death of Leggatt to free his own conscience from accusations of cowardice during the typhoon? How strong is the narrator's Chief Mate who likes to account for everything, and how much of the Cain does he have in him when he goes to pieces under the blackness of Koh-ring? Precisely this kind of ambivalence characterizes the use of the echoed archetypal structure in *The Secret Sharer.* Thus the narrator as Cain *must kill* Abel-Leggatt in order that he may come to mature moral terms with his ship, crew, and self; and as Abel he *must not kill* or shame his first mate and crew in order that the trial be successfully passed.

The echo structure, by identifying various members of the ship's company now as Cain and now as Abel, suggests that all men in the ship-world are both Cain and Abel, that the Cain-Abel personality dwells in every man. "I wondered," says the narrator, "how far I should turn out faithful to that ideal conception of one's own personality every man sets up for himself secretly." And as the final structure in the novel suggests, the narrator meets his Cain personality in the form of Leggatt and in the form of his own blubbering Chief Mate and conquers both, dramatically answering his own question. Seeing Leggatt's phosphorescent flash pass under the white hat he wears into the water, the narrator thinks, "But I hardly thought of my other self, now gone from the ship, to be hidden for ever from all friendly faces, *to be a fugitive and a vagabond on the earth, with no brand of the curse on his sane forehead to stay a slay-ing hand . . . too proud to explain."*

Less explicit than the Cain-Abel archetypal structure is that of the Jonah archetype which appears in somewhat shadowy form in *The Secret Sharer* but which creates an echo structure nevertheless. During the fierce typhoon Leggatt kills the muti-nous sailor, as he reminds us, a "miserable devil." Then he de-scribes the mounting fury of the storm which follows hard upon his act:

And the ship running for her life, touch and go all the time, any minute her last in a sea fit to turn your hair grey only a-looking at it. I under-stand that the skipper, too, started raving like the rest of them. The man had been deprived of sleep for more than a week, and to have this sprung on him at the height of a furious gale nearly drove him out of his mind. *I wonder they didn't fling me overboard after getting the carcass of their precious ship-mate out of my fingers.* They had rather a job to separate us, I've been told. A sufficiently fierce story to make an old judge and a respectable jury sit up a bit.

This first part of the structure is about one half of the Jonah archetype: the fierce storm, the cursed or pursued or immoral person whose actions are intimately connected with the howling typhoon, the breach of a moral code, the suggestion of being thrown overboard, the hint at judgment. The final half of the archetypal pattern appears many pages later when at the end of the novel the echo structure completes the archetype. The nar-rator-captain has made a decision to put Leggatt overboard:

"Now," I whispered, loudly, into the saloon—too loudly, perhaps, but I was afraid I couldn't make a sound. He was by my side in an instant— *the double captain slipped past the stairs—through the tiny dark passage . . . a sliding door. We were in the sail-locker, scrambling on our knees over the sails.* A sudden thought struck me. *I saw myself wandering bare-footed, bareheaded, the sun beating on my dark poll.* I snatched off my floppy hat and tried hurriedly in the dark to ram it on my other self. He dodged and fended off silently. I wonder what he thought had come to me before he understood and suddenly desisted. Our hands met gropingly, lingered united in a steady, motionless clasp for a second. . . . No word was breathed by either of us when they separated.

Returning to the deck, the narrator looks about on the sea for

some marker which will indicate the position of the ship as it
begins its turn from the land:

All at once my strained, yearning stare distinguished a white object floating within a yard of the ship's side. White on the black water. A phosphorescent flash passed under it. What was that thing? . . . I recognised
my own floppy hat. It must have fallen off his head . . . and he didn't
bother. Now I had what I wanted—the saving mark for my eyes.

Thus at the last moment before the turn toward resolution
in the novel, the second half of the echo structure is completed
when Leggatt leaves the ship so that she may save herself and
he himself. But the novel suggests more than this. Since Leggatt
is to be saved from immediate death, since the suggestiveness of
the sail-locker scene evokes the atmosphere of the belly of the
whale into which Jonah descended and from which he was to
be released, since the ship releases him into the waters of freedom, and since the narrator himself is released from his Cain
(Leggatt) personality in the sail-locker scene ("I saw myself
wandering barefooted, bareheaded, the sun beating on my dark
poll"), the echo part of the structure seems to identify the ship
as an archetypal image of Jonah's whale. At the same time the
Cain-Abel archetype passes through the Jonah archetype when
the narrator thinks of himself as wandering unprotected over
the face of the earth. The significance of this crossing of archetypes lies, I believe, in the identification of common elements
between Jonah as wanderer and Cain as wanderer. The former
refused to carry out the commands of his God; the latter broke
the commandments of his God by killing his brother.

What then is the significance of the Jonah archetype which
we have seen is split into several parts, the first appearing near
the beginning of *The Secret Sharer,* the second part, the echo
structure, appearing on the last page of the novel? The archetype, for one thing, gives meaning to experience, those traditional meanings which cluster about the Cain and Abel story
and, in the immediate situation, the Jonah story. The echoed
archetype especially gives a kind of continuity to fragmentary,
splintered, or shattered actions, movements, or partial patterns
of behavior. It makes sense out of the meaninglessness of dispa-

rate experiences by giving recognizable form to discontinuous, perhaps chaotic experiences. The Biblical archetypes establish a moral climate within whose atmosphere the actions of the story may be judged. The archetype ritualizes, congeals, makes cohere, for instance, those scattered, almost senseless actions of men. To this, however, it brings its own meaning from the tradition of which it is a part. The way Leggatt is significantly identified as Jonah and the way the narrator is also identified as Jonah must now be examined.

Aboard the narrator's ship, Leggatt gradually poisons the relationship between the narrator and his crew. In the becalmed sea, a direct reversal of the typhoon scene, the threat of the presence of this Jonah to the narrator and his ship is as great as the threat to the *Sephora* and Captain Archbold in the howling storm. Jonah's moral weakness arose from his disobedience; Leggatt's moral defection lies in his murderous disposition, his inability to live within the strict confines of a moral atmosphere, and his essentially nihilistic attitude toward inferiors: "Miserable devils that have no business to live at all." Jonah flees his Lord; Leggatt flees from the captain's retribution and from the threat of law. Jonah, after spending three days in the whale, is coughed up and reconciled with his God; Leggatt after spending a number of days in the narrator's cabin, bathroom, and sail-locker, is lowered into the water signalizing the reconciliation of the narrator with that other part of himself, the moral, controlled, ethical forces with the threatening, amoral forces of his personality.

The Jonah archetype like the Cain-Abel archetype contributes another dimension to the novel and reinforces its central thesis by suggesting in "other words" the very same thing that the Cain-Abel archetype suggested. Every man potentially *is* Cain and *is* Abel or every man *is* Jonah (Cain and Abel in one configuration); every man must come to terms with the other personality lurking within the human flesh. But, and this is most important, the Cain-Abel archetype suddenly crosses or is superimposed on the Jonah archetype in the sail-locker scene. As suggested, this correspondence of archetypes seems to hint that essentially the two are one archetype told in different terms.

Thus murder and disobedience are deliberately confused by
means of the fusion of the archetypes, and they become, in terms
of the thematic development of the novel, symbolic of any moral
weakness which would not permit man to know his most secret
self and the constant threat which that inner self imposes on
personality. Leggatt does not have the brand of Cain on him,
the echo structure suggests and the narrator says at one moment
near the end of *The Secret Sharer,* "with no brand of the curse
on his sane forehead to stay a slaying hand." Leggatt does swim
from the ship-whale, however, identified as the Cain who is condemned to wander the earth even if incognito "now gone from
the ship, to be hidden for ever from all friendly faces, to be a
fugitive and a vagabond on the earth. . . ." At the moment the
two archetypes cross, while the men are in the darkened sail-
locker, Leggatt assumes his role once more in the Cain-Abel
archetype; and the narrator assumes the role of Jonah in the
second archetype. Symbolically this transference is achieved
when the narrator claps his hat on the head of the reluctant
Leggatt and when their hands meet for a final identification and
farewell. The narrator arises to pace the deck of his ship-world
no longer the disobedient Jonah within the punishing whale.
He returns to the deck in the symbolic role of the obedient Jonah from that sail-locker belly to assume full command of himself, of his men, and of his ship.

Anyone familiar with archetypal structures will observe immediately that another archetype complicates the two discussed
here by overlaying them with suggestions of Leggatt as scapegoat. As Kenneth Burke describes the archetypal function of
this device, the scapegoat is "the 'representative' or 'vessel' of
certain unwanted evils, the sacrificial animal upon whose back
the burden of these evils is ritualistically loaded . . . the tend-
ency was to endow the sacrificial animal with social coordinates,
so that the goat became replaced by the 'sacrificial King.'" The
conditions for becoming the archetypal scapegoat are any of
these:

(1) He may be made worthy legalistically (i.e., by making him an of-
fender against legal or moral justice so that he "deserves" what he gets).
(2) We may make him worthy by leading towards sacrifice fatalistically

(as when we so point the arrows of the plot that the audience comes to think of him as a marked man, and so prepares itself to relinquish him). . . .

(3) We may make him worthy by a subtle kind of poetic justice, in making the sacrificial vessel "too good for this world," hence the *highest* value, hence the *most perfect* sacrifice (as with the Christ theme, and its secular variants, such as little Hanno Buddenbrooks, whose exceptional sensitivity to music made him worthy to be sacrificed to music).[5]

Clearly Leggatt is the scapegoat for Captain Archbold and for the narrator as well. In the case of the captain of the *Sephora* Leggatt fulfills the first of the three conditions. By offending against legal justice when he kills the devilish sailor, Leggatt becomes "worthy legalistically" for sacrifice. But his guilt is complicated and mitigated because of his relation with Captain Archbold, for the captain uses him as a "vessel" for his own lack of bravery, for his own going to pieces when the ship appeared lost, and for his sense of guilt in front of his crew and wife. In the latter sense, then, the damning legal condemnation must be ameliorated and Leggatt, the legal murderer, must be seen as something less than a criminal. This scapegoat does, after all, save the *Sephora* and the lives of everyone on board including that of Captain Archbold, who performs the sacrifice of his scapegoat by putting him down a suicide.

For the narrator Leggatt serves as a scapegoat by fulfilling the two final conditions of the archetypal structure. Leggatt is led "towards sacrifice fatalistically" because the reader is constantly reminded that he represents Cain, that he destroys the harmony of the narrator's ship, that he prevents order from being established, and that he is the metaphorical scorpion threateningly present. It is not guilt or a sense of guilt or jealousy or evil which the narrator transfers to him as he places his hat on his head in that sail-locker scene. It is something more subtle and more elusive. This scapegoat is a reminder to the narrator at the outset of his taking command of his first ship that all men have within them the very great possibility of another "presence" which in times of trial will defeat the outer self, the social mask

<hr>

[5] Kenneth Burke, *The Philosophy of Literary Form* (New York, 1957), pp. 34-35. I am indebted not only to this book but also to all Professor Burke's work for constant stimulation.

constructed for our relationships with other men, unless the presence and its threat is met and conquered. The "secret self," Leggatt, struggles for a moment in the darkness of the sail-locker (whale's belly), trying to fend off the hat, but the narrator defeats him there and places it firmly on his head. In the same way he will defeat his own threatening obtuseness when he returns to deck and seizes and shakes strength into his be-whiskered Chief Mate.

As a fulfillment of the final condition, Conrad draws Leggatt as worthy of the sacrifice, with overtones of great reluctance on the part of the narrator. First, he is identified with the narrator whose own personality we admire. Then through a piling up of detail, Conrad builds a case for our admiration of Leggatt, and this in spite of the murder. He is, for instance, "a strong soul"; his father is "a parson"; he and the narrator are "Conway" boys. The narrator thinks, "And I knew well enough also that my double there was no homicidal ruffian." Leggatt does not despair nor does he think of suicide when he is certain that he is lost, although Captain Archbold will make him a suicide to clear his records and conscience. Leggatt refuses to try to break out of the *Sephora* in a violent manner because, "somebody would have got killed for certain, and I did not want any of that." The narrator marvels "at that something unyielding in his character which was carrying him through so finely." And, finally, the last statement of the novel, a deliberate ambiguity referring to both the narrator and Leggatt, "A free man, a proud swimmer *striking out* for *a new destiny*." In this way and because he frees the narrator from the threat of defections of self, Leggatt is the most perfect sacrifice, the scapegoat of the highest value.

The sail-locker scene is crucial to an understanding of the functioning of archetypal patterns. Here the three patterns suddenly coalesce and when they separate thematic relevance has been resolved. Until the transfer of the hat, Cain, Abel, Jonah, and scapegoat relationships are mingled and fused into each other. Then the hat is pushed down on Leggatt's head, the three archetypes separate, and the story plunges toward its climax, each archetypal role clearly distinguishable from all others.

The fundamental thematic tensions in *The Secret Sharer* are embodied in and conveyed by these overlapping archetypal patterns. The knowledge which the narrator must gain, that he has lurking within himself the possibilities of moral corruption, represented by Leggatt and his attitude towards humanity, and the narrator's being tested, is carried in the Cain-Abel archetype which creates for the narrator a situation similar to that created for Leggatt. But by failing to pass his initiatory test successfully, Leggatt remains a Cain figure. By passing his test successfully the narrator faces his Cain characteristics and subjects them to his will. The Jonah archetype is introduced to suggest reconciliation by showing the two figures re-united in one person who carries with him the moral background of the Biblical tradition from which the archetype came. The possibility of danger and threat to those intimately related to Jonah as he seeks to flee is suggested by Leggatt's flight from the *Sephora* and his gradual disruption of the narrator's relationship with his men. But the possibility of salvation through a period of suffering and willingness to admit to and rid oneself of certain defections, and the possibility of undergoing a test of the reintegrated personality is portrayed in and symbolized by the narrator's shifting to the leading role in the Jonah archetype. As the reborn Jonah arose from the belly of the whale successfully reconciled with his God, so too the fully reintegrated narrator climbs from the sail locker a new person to face and pass his test victoriously.

COMMENT

The idea of the echo structure, examined in "The Secret Sharer," may be used as a guide through other short stories and novels of Joseph Conrad. The student will find that in *The Heart of Darkness* Conrad has established one story or situation which he rehearses a number of times. It is first seen in its complete development in the parable of the Romans who entered the wilds of Britain and brought civilization to the natives; it is echoed in Marlow's trip to the Sepulchral City; echoed once more in his trip to Africa; echoed again in the journey into the grove of death, the journey to the interior, the journey to Kurtz, and so forth. But each echo contributes something new to the first telling of the story. Then each of these journeys is an archetypal situation, much like the journey of the mythical hero Theseus into the labyrinth in order to deliver man from the Minotaur (symbolically some threat to personal development, to freedom of thought, to the progress of humanity). Then the various men whom Marlow meets are "echoes" (sometimes inverted) of each other—some are repetitions of others with significant differences. The scapegoat situation is echoed with a number of characters, especially Marlow and Kurtz, but there is at least one other. The initial parable of the Romans is repeated in various forms within a number of the journey echoes, each repetition contributing significantly to the meaning of the story.

Of other stories by Conrad, "The Lagoon" should be examined for its echo structure—it is considerably less complex than *The Heart of Darkness*. The short novel *The Nigger of the Narcissus* is a notable example of the method.

VII

The Bride Comes to Yellow Sky

STEPHEN CRANE

I

The great Pullman was whirling onward with such dignity of motion that a glance from the window seemed simply to prove that the plains of Texas were pouring eastward. Vast flats of green grass, dull-hued spaces of mesquite and cactus, little groups of frame houses, woods of light and tender trees, all were sweeping into the east, sweeping over the horizon, a precipice.

A newly married pair had boarded this coach at San Antonio. The man's face was reddened from many days in the wind and sun, and a direct result of his new black clothes was that his brick-colored hands were constantly performing in a most conscious fashion. From time to time he looked down respectfully at his attire. He sat with a hand on each knee, like a man waiting in a barber's shop. The glances he devoted to other passengers were furtive and shy.

The bride was not pretty, nor was she very young. She wore a dress of blue cashmere, with small reservations of velvet here and there and with steel buttons abounding. She continually twisted her head to regard her puff sleeves, very stiff, straight, and high. They embarrassed her. It was quite apparent that she had cooked, and that she expected to cook, dutifully. The blushes caused by the careless scrutiny of some passengers as she had entered the car were strange to see upon this plain, under-class countenance, which was drawn in placid, almost emotionless lines.

They were evidently very happy. "Ever been in a parlor-car before?" he asked, smiling with delight.

"No," she answered. "I never was. It's fine, ain't it?"

"Great! And then after a while we'll go forward to the diner and get a big lay-out. Finest meal in the world. Charge a dollar."

"Oh, do they?" cried the bride. "Charge a dollar? Why, that's too much—for us—ain't it, Jack?"

"Not this trip, anyhow," he answered bravely. "We're going to go the whole thing."

Later, he explained to her about the trains. "You see, it's a thousand miles from one end of Texas to the other, and this train runs right across it and never stops but four times." He had the pride of an owner. He pointed out to her the dazzling fittings of the coach, and in truth her eyes opened wider as she contemplated the sea-green figured velvet, the shining brass, silver, and glass, the wood that gleamed as darkly brilliant as the surface of a pool of oil. At one end a bronze figure sturdily held a support for a separated chamber, and at convenient places on the ceiling were frescoes in olive and silver.

To the minds of the pair, their surroundings reflected the glory of their marriage that morning in San Antonio. This was the environment of their new estate, and the man's face in particular beamed with an elation that made him appear ridiculous to the negro porter. This individual at times surveyed them from afar with an amused and superior grin. On other occasions he bullied them with skill in ways that did not make it exactly plain to them that they were being bullied. He subtly used all the manners of the most unconquerable kind of snobbery. He oppressed them, but of this oppression they had small knowledge, and they speedily forgot that infrequently a number of travellers covered them with stares of derisive enjoyment. Historically there was supposed to be something infinitely humorous in their situation.

"We are due in Yellow Sky at 3 · 42," he said, looking tenderly into her eyes.

"Oh, are we?" she said, as if she had not been aware of it. To evince surprise at her husband's statement was part of her wifely amiability. She took from a pocket a little silver watch, and as she held it before her and stared at it with a frown of attention, the new husband's face shone.

"I bought it in San Anton' from a friend of mine," he told her gleefully.

"It's seventeen minutes past twelve," she said, looking up at him with a kind of shy and clumsy coquetry. A passenger, noting this play, grew excessively sardonic, and winked at himself in one of the numerous mirrors.

At last they went to the dining-car. Two rows of negro waiters, in glowing white suits, surveyed their entrance with the interest and also the equanimity of men who had been forewarned. The pair fell to the lot of a waiter who happened to feel pleasure in steering them through their meal. He viewed them with the manner of a fatherly pilot, his countenance radiant with benevolence. The patronage, entwined with the ordinary deference, was not plain to them. And yet, as they returned to their coach, they showed in their faces a sense of escape.

To the left, miles down a long purple slope, was a little ribbon of mist where moved the keening Rio Grande. The train was approaching it at an angle, and the apex was Yellow Sky. Presently it was apparent that, as the distance from Yellow Sky grew shorter, the husband became commensurately restless. His brick-red hands were more insistent in their prominence. Occasionally he was even rather absent-minded and far-away when the bride leaned forward and addressed him.

As a matter of truth, Jack Potter was beginning to find the shadow of a deed weigh upon him like a leaden slab. He, the town marshal of Yellow Sky, a man known, liked, and feared in his corner, a prominent person, had gone to San Antonio to meet a girl he believed he loved, and there, after the usual prayers, had actually induced her to marry him, without consulting Yellow Sky for any part of the transaction. He was now bringing his bride before an innocent and unsuspecting community.

Of course, people in Yellow Sky married as it pleased them,

in accordance with a general custom; but such was Potter's thought of his duty to his friends, or of their idea of his duty, or of an unspoken form which does not control men in these matters, that he felt he was heinous. He had committed an extraordinary crime. Face to face with this girl in San Antonio, and spurred by his sharp impulse, he had gone headlong over all the social hedges. At San Antonio he was like a man hidden in the dark. A knife to sever any friendly duty, any form, was easy to his hand in that remote city. But the hour of Yellow Sky, the hour of daylight, was approaching.

He knew full well that his marriage was an important thing to his town. It could only be exceeded by the burning of the new hotel. His friends could not forgive him. Frequently he had reflected on the advisability of telling them by telegraph, but a new cowardice had been upon him. He feared to do it. And now the train was hurrying him toward a scene of amazement, glee, and reproach. He glanced out of the window at the line of haze swinging slowly in towards the train.

Yellow Sky had a kind of brass band, which played painfully, to the delight of the populace. He laughed without heart as he thought of it. If the citizens could dream of his prospective arrival with his bride, they would parade the band at the station and escort them, amid cheers and laughing congratulations, to his adobe home.

He resolved that he would use all the devices of speed and plains-craft in making the journey from the station to his house. Once within that safe citadel, he could issue some sort of vocal bulletin, and then not go among the citizens until they had time to wear off a little of their enthusiasm.

The bride looked anxiously at him. "What's worrying you, Jack?"

He laughed again. "I'm not worrying, girl. I'm only thinking of Yellow Sky."

She flushed in comprehension.

A sense of mutual guilt invaded their minds and developed a finer tenderness. They looked at each other with eyes softly aglow. But Potter often laughed the same nervous laugh. The flush upon the bride's face seemed quite permanent.

The traitor to the feelings of Yellow Sky narrowly watched the speeding landscape. "We're nearly there," he said.

Presently the porter came and announced the proximity of Potter's home. He held a brush in his hand and, with all his airy superiority gone, he brushed Potter's new clothes as the latter slowly turned this way and that way. Potter fumbled out a coin and gave it to the porter, as he had seen others do. It was a heavy and muscle-bound business, as that of a man shoeing his first horse.

The porter took their bag, and as the train began to slow they moved forward to the hooded platform of the car. Presently the two engines and their long string of coaches rushed into the station of Yellow Sky.

"They have to take water here," said Potter, from a constricted throat and in mournful cadence, as one announcing death. Before the train stopped, his eye had swept the length of the platform, and he was glad and astonished to see there was none upon it but the station-agent, who, with a slightly hurried and anxious air, was walking toward the water-tanks. When the train had halted, the porter alighted first and placed in position a little temporary step.

"Come on, girl," said Potter hoarsely. As he helped her down they each laughed on a false note. He took the bag from the negro, and bade his wife cling to his arm. As they slunk rapidly away, his hang-dog glance perceived that they were unloading the two trunks, and also that the station-agent far ahead near the baggage-car had turned and was running towards him, making gestures. He laughed, and groaned as he laughed, when he noted the first effect of his marital bliss upon Yellow Sky. He gripped his wife's arm firmly to his side, and they fled. Behind them the porter stood chuckling fatuously.

II

The California Express on the Southern Railway was due at Yellow Sky in twenty-one minutes. There were six men at the bar of the "Weary Gentleman" saloon. One was a drummer who talked a great deal and rapidly; three were Texans who did not care to talk at that time; and two were Mexican sheep-

herders who did not talk as a general practice in the "Weary
Gentleman" saloon. The barkeeper's dog lay on the board walk
that crossed in front of the door. His head was on his paws, and
he glanced drowsily here and there with the constant vigilance
of a dog that is kicked on occasion. Across the sandy street were
some vivid green grass plots, so wonderful in appearance amid
the sands that burned near them in a blazing sun that they
caused a doubt in the mind. They exactly resembled the grass
mats used to represent lawns on the stage. At the cooler end of
the railway station a man without a coat sat in a tilted chair
and smoked his pipe. The fresh-cut bank of the Rio Grande
circled near the town, and there could be seen beyond it a great,
plum-colored plain of mesquite.

Save for the busy drummer and his companions in the saloon,
Yellow Sky was dozing. The new-comer leaned gracefully upon
the bar, and recited many tales with the confidence of a bard
who has come upon a new field.

"—and at the moment that the old man fell down stairs with
the bureau in his arms, the old woman was coming up with
two scuttles of coal, and, of course—"

The drummer's tale was interrupted by a young man who
suddenly appeared in the open door. He cried: "Scratchy Wilson's drunk, and has turned loose with both hands." The two
Mexicans at once set down their glasses and faded out of the
rear entrance of the saloon.

The drummer, innocent and jocular, answered: "All right,
old man. S'pose he has. Come in and have a drink, anyhow."

But the information had made such an obvious cleft in every
skull in the room that the drummer was obliged to see its importance. All had become instantly solemn. "Say," said he, mystified, "what is this?" His three companions made the introductory gesture of eloquent speech, but the young man at the
door forestalled them.

"It means, my friend," he answered, as he came into the saloon, "that for the next two hours this town won't be a health
resort."

The barkeeper went to the door and locked and barred it.
Reaching out of the window, he pulled in heavy wooden shut-

ters and barred them. Immediately a solemn, chapel-like gloom was upon the place. The drummer was looking from one to another.

"But, say," he cried, "what is this, anyhow? You don't mean there is going to be a gun-fight?"

"Don't know whether there'll be a fight or not," answered one man grimly. "But there'll be some shootin'—some good shootin'."

The young man who had warned them waved his hand. "Oh, there'll be a fight fast enough, if anyone wants it. Anybody can get a fight out there in the street. There's a fight just waiting."

The drummer seemed to be swayed between the interest of a foreigner and a perception of personal danger.

"What did you say his name was?" he asked.

"Scratchy Wilson," they answered in chorus.

"And will he kill anybody? What are you going to do? Does this happen often? Does he rampage around like this once a week or so? Can he break in that door?"

"No, he can't break down that door," replied the barkeeper. "He's tried it three times. But when he comes you'd better lay down on the floor, stranger. He's dead sure to shoot at it, and a bullet may come through."

Thereafter the drummer kept a strict eye upon the door. The time had not yet been called for him to hug the floor, but, as a minor precaution, he sidled near to the wall. "Will he kill anybody?" he said again.

The men laughed low and scornfully at the question.

"He's out to shoot, and he's out for trouble. Don't see any good in experimentin' with him."

"But what do you do in a case like this? What do you do?"

A man responded: "Why, he and Jack Potter—"

"But," in chorus, the other men interrupted, "Jack Potter's in San Anton'."

"Well, who is he? What's he got to do with it?"

"Oh, he's the town marshal. He goes out and fights Scratchy when he gets on one of these tears."

"Wow," said the drummer, mopping his brow. "Nice job he's got."

The voices had toned away to mere whisperings. The drummer wished to ask further questions which were born of an increasing anxiety and bewilderment; but when he attempted them, the men merely looked at him in irritation and motioned him to remain silent. A tense waiting hush was upon them. In the deep shadows of the room their eyes shone as they listened for sounds from the street. One man made three gestures at the barkeeper, and the latter, moving like a ghost, handed him a glass and a bottle. The man poured a full glass of whisky, and set down the bottle noiselessly. He gulped the whisky in a swallow, and turned again towards the door in immovable silence. The drummer saw that the barkeeper, without a sound, had taken a Winchester from beneath the bar. Later he saw this individual beckoning to him, so he tiptoed across the room.

"You better come with me back of the bar."

"No, thanks," said the drummer, perspiring. "I'd rather be where I can make a break for the back door."

Whereupon the man of bottles made a kindly but peremptory gesture. The drummer obeyed it, and finding himself seated on a box with his head below the level of the bar, balm was laid upon his soul at sight of various zinc and copper fittings that bore a resemblance to armor-plate. The barkeeper took a seat comfortably upon an adjacent box.

"You see," he whispered, "this here Scratchy Wilson is a wonder with a gun—a perfect wonder—and when he goes on the war trail, we hunt our holes—naturally. He's about the last one of the old gang that used to hang out along the river here. He's a terror when he's drunk. When he's sober he's all right— kind of simple—wouldn't hurt a fly—nicest fellow in town. But when he's drunk—whoo!"

There were periods of stillness. "I wish Jack Potter was back from San Anton'," said the barkeeper. "He shot Wilson up once—in the leg—and he would sail in and pull out the kinks in this thing."

Presently they heard from a distance the sound of a shot, followed by three wild yowls. It instantly removed a bond from the men in the darkened saloon. There was a shuffling of feet. They looked at each other. "Here he comes," they said.

III

A man in a maroon-colored flannel shirt, which had been purchased for purposes of decoration and made, principally, by some Jewish women on the east side of New York, rounded a corner and walked into the middle of the main street of Yellow Sky. In either hand the man held a long, heavy, blue-black revolver. Often he yelled, and these cries rang through a semblance of a deserted village, shrilly flying over the roofs in a volume that seemed to have no relation to the ordinary vocal strength of a man. It was as if the surrounding stillness formed the arch of a tomb over him. These cries of ferocious challenge rang against walls of silence. And his boots had red tops with gilded imprints, of the kind beloved in winter by little sledding boys on the hillsides of New England.

The man's face flamed in a rage begot of whisky. His eyes, rolling and yet keen for ambush, hunted the still doorways and windows. He walked with the creeping movement of the midnight cat. As it occurred to him, he roared menacing information. The long revolvers in his hands were as easy as straws; they were moved with an electric swiftness. The little fingers of each hand played sometimes in a musician's way. Plain from the low collar of the shirt, the cords of his neck straightened and sank, straightened and sank, as passion moved him. The only sounds were his terrible invitations. The calm adobes preserved their demeanor at the passing of this small thing in the middle of the street.

There was no offer of fight; no offer of fight. The man called to the sky. There were no attractions. He bellowed and fumed and swayed his revolvers here and everywhere.

The dog of the barkeeper of the "Weary Gentleman" saloon had not appreciated the advance of events. He yet lay dozing in front of his master's door. At sight of the dog, the man paused and raised his revolver humorously. At sight of the man, the dog sprang up and walked diagonally away, with a sullen head, and growling. The man yelled, and the dog broke into a gallop. As it was about to enter an alley, there was a loud noise, a whistling, and something spat the ground directly before it. The dog screamed, and, wheeling in terror, galloped headlong in a new direction. Again there was a noise, a whistling, and sand was kicked viciously before it. Fear-stricken, the dog turned and flurried like an animal in a pen. The man stood laughing, his weapons at his hips.

Ultimately the man was attracted by the closed door of the "Weary Gentleman" saloon. He went to it, and hammering with a revolver, demanded drink.

The door remaining imperturbable, he picked a bit of paper from the walk and nailed it to the framework with a knife. He then turned his back contemptuously upon this popular resort, and walking to the opposite side of the street, and spinning there on his heel quickly and lithely, fired at the bit of paper. He missed it by a half-inch. He swore at himself, and went away. Later, he comfortably fusilladed the windows of his most intimate friend. The man was playing with this town. It was a toy for him.

But still there was no offer of fight. The name of Jack Potter, his ancient antagonist, entered his mind, and he concluded that it would be a glad thing if he should go to Potter's house and by bombardment induce him to come out and fight. He moved in the direction of his desire, chanting Apache scalp-music.

When he arrived at it, Potter's house presented the same still front as had the other adobes. Taking up a strategic position, the man howled a challenge. But this house regarded him as might a great stone god. It gave no sign. After a decent wait, the man howled further challenges, mingling with them wonderful epithets.

Presently there came the spectacle of a man churning himself into deepest rage over the immobility of a house. He fumed at it as the winter wind attacks a prairie cabin in the North. To the distance there should have gone the sound of a tumult like the fighting of 200 Mexicans. As necessity bade him, he paused for breath or to reload his revolvers.

IV

Potter and his bride walked sheepishly and with speed. Sometimes they laughed together shamefacedly and low.

"Next corner, dear," he said finally.

They put forth the efforts of a pair walking bowed against a strong wind. Potter was about to raise a finger to point the first appearance of the new home when, as they circled the corner, they came face to face with a man in a maroon-colored shirt who was feverishly pushing cartridges into a large revolver. Upon the instant the man dropped his revolver to the ground, and, like lightning, whipped another from its holster. The second weapon was aimed at the bridegroom's chest.

There was a silence. Potter's mouth seemed to be merely a grave for his tongue. He exhibited an instinct to at once loosen his arm from the woman's grip, and he dropped the bag to the sand. As for the bride, her face had gone as yellow as old cloth. She was a slave to hideous rites gazing at the apparitional snake.

The two men faced each other at a distance of three paces. He of the revolver smiled with a new and quiet ferocity.

"Tried to sneak up on me," he said. "Tried to sneak up on me!" His eyes grew more baleful. As Potter made a slight movement, the man thrust his revolver venomously forward. "No, don't you do it, Jack Potter. Don't you move a finger toward a gun just yet. Don't you move an eyelash. The time has come for me to settle with you, and I'm goin' to do it my own way and loaf along with no interferin'. So if you don't want a gun bent on you, just mind what I tell you."

Potter looked at his enemy. "I ain't got a gun on me Scratchy," he said. "Honest, I ain't." He was stiffening and steadying, but yet somewhere at the back of his mind a vision of the Pullman floated; the sea-green figured velvet, the shining brass, silver, and glass, the wood that gleamed as darkly brilliant as the surface of a pool of oil—all the glory of the marriage, the environment of the new estate. "You know I fight when it comes to fighting, Scratchy Wilson, but I ain't got a gun on me. You'll have to do all the shootin' yourself."

His enemy's face went livid. He stepped forward and lashed his weapon to and fro before Potter's chest. "Don't you tell me you ain't got no gun on you, you whelp. Don't tell me no lie like that. There ain't a man in Texas ever seen you without no gun. Don't take me for no kid." His eyes blazed with light, and his throat worked like a pump.

"I ain't takin' you for no kid," answered Potter. His heels had not moved an inch backward. "I'm takin' you for a —— fool. I tell you I ain't got a gun, and I ain't. If you're goin' to shoot me up, you better begin now. You'll never get a chance like this again."

So much enforced reasoning had told on Wilson's rage. He was calmer. "If you ain't got a gun, why ain't you got a gun?" he sneered. "Been to Sunday-school?"

"I ain't got a gun because I've just come from San Anton' with my wife. I'm married," said Potter. "And if I'd thought there was going to be any galoots like you prowling around when I brought my wife home, I'd had a gun, and don't you forget it."

"Married!" said Scratchy, not at all comprehending.

"Yes, married. I'm married," said Potter distinctly.

"Married?" said Scratchy. Seemingly for the first time he saw the drooping, drowning woman at the other man's side. "No!" he said. He was like a creature allowed a glimpse of another world. He moved a pace backward, and his arm with the revolver dropped to his side. "Is this the lady?" he asked.

"Yes, this is the lady," answered Potter.

There was another period of silence.

"Well," said Wilson at last, slowly, "I s'pose it's all off now."

"It's all off if you say so, Scratchy. You know I didn't make the trouble." Potter lifted his valise.

"Well, I 'low it's off, Jack," said Wilson. He was looking at the ground. "Married!" He was not a student of chivalry; it was merely that in the presence of this foreign condition he was a simple child of the earlier plains. He picked up his starboard revolver, and placing both weapons in their holsters, he went away. His feet made funnel-shaped tracks in the heavy sand.

Stephen Crane's "The Bride Comes to Yellow Sky"

GEORGE MONTEIRO

Few readers will deny that one of Crane's deliberate purposes in "The Bride Comes to Yellow Sky" was to satirize the conventional, popular-magazine story of a romanticized American West. With quite different intention from that of Bret Harte or Owen Wister, he worked through the stylized form for this story of the basic conflict of lawman versus outlaw leading to the denouement of a bittersweet gundown in the open street. Crane's approach, enabling him to manipulate the preconceptions of his audience concerning his basic Western materials, led to the deflation of customary form rather than its fulfillment—after the turmoil, the shouting, and the promise of violence, the showdown turns into a startling talkdown. Beyond this, Crane was able, through his characteristic use of irony, to invest the stereotype for the frontier-story with his own brand of psychological realism.

Yet despite his satiric purpose, Crane did skirt perilously close to the disasters of literary and historical sentimentality. By 1897, when Crane wrote "The Bride," much of the frontier quality of the West had disappeared in the face of Eastern encroachment; and there is enough in Crane's story to establish this passing as one of his secondary themes. In the omnisciently presented vision of the opening paragraph, "the plains of Texas," seen from the moving train, "were pouring eastward." Moreover, the theme of Eastern usurpation is reinforced when Crane tells us that even the outlaw's ceremonial dress is composed in part of a shirt "which had been purchased for purposes of decoration and made, principally, by some Jewish women on the east side

of New York" and a pair of boots whose "red tops with gilded
imprints" were "of the kind beloved in winter by little sledding
boys on the hillsides of New England." Besides the sure sense
of ironic deflation, these phrases reveal Crane's perception that
it was Eastern technology and mercantilism that had overcome
the less ordered economy of the West. In itself this observation
could not have been striking even in Crane's day. But as a theme
it is handmaiden to the rendering of a larger, more inclusive
meaning.

The core of the action Crane presents deals with the metamorphosis and growth of one form of human community out
of another. It is not casual that the adjective which appears
most frequently in this story is *new*. Virtually as a motif, this
word is invariably associated with the marshal, his marriage,
and the signs of a new order. The story opens with a sense of
movement and rush which threatens full destruction. In dreamlike flood, besides "the plains of Texas," flats, spaces, frame
houses, and light, tender trees are "sweeping into the east,
sweeping over the horizon, a precipice." The story closes with
the "simple child of the earlier plains"—"his feet [making] funnel-shaped tracks in the heavy sand," moving slowly but irrev-
ocably away over a horizon that suggests another precipice.
Having opened with a vision of the double-strand of civilization and nature moving before the "great Pullman," "The
Bride" ends with the demise of the individual who finally stands
alone for an older alliance of man with nature; as the reminder,
in fact, of an attenuated, if still unbroken, connection.

The story is concerned further with a central opposition that
can be described in different ways. Under the largest rubric of
Society-Nature, this conflict appears as domestication and wildness, order and chaos, law and disorder. In the specific details
of the story, however, they can and do appear as silence, speech,
reason—noise, music, emotion; these are, in turn, aligned dramatically with house and street, railroad and river, and, finally,
marshal and drunk. The tension generated by these oppositions
is, of course, epitomized in the single external conflict of Jack
Potter and Scratchy Wilson. But thematic opposition is manifested in still other actions and situations.

Crane divides his story into four sections. In Part I, Potter and the Bride are out of place on the train from San Antonio. In the parlor car, the "environment" of their greatest discomfort, they are "bullied" in a relatively gentle way by the porter. The parlor car as the icon for the "new estate" in Part I is transformed into the "Weary Gentleman" saloon of Parts II and III. As a sign of the established order of Yellow Sky, the saloon is opposed to the street. Within the saloon, identified imagistically with the parlor car (as will be demonstrated later), the "town" is incarcerated at the pleasure of Wilson the badman. The climactic confrontation, however, is to take place between the marshal and the badman. Therefore, when Wilson himself does not appear in Part I, the functions of his role are assumed by the Negro porter who answers Potter's own laughter by "chuckling fatuously" behind him as he flees the coach. The victory here is at the marshal's expense. In Parts II and III, however, it is Potter who does not appear, while Wilson himself gains victory over the inmates of the saloon and over the barkeeper's dog, with whom Wilson later associates the marshal. In Part IV, Potter finally comes up against Wilson, and the man who has been bullied by the porter of the "new estate," now, because he too is committed to that estate, wins out over the badman who had bullied the entire town. The whole action of the story, then, along with its designated parts, turns around a series of conflicts between bullies completely armed with guns or manners, depending upon the occasion, and victims who are at a total disadvantage.

Consequently, it can be seen that it is the particular code by which each individual wishes the conflict to be fought that determines whether he is to be victim or victor. In the parlor-car world Potter is victim because choosing to live by the manners and mores of that world, he is at the moment less qualified to do so than the porter or the other passengers, for example, the one who, amused at the bridal couple, "winked at himself in one of the numerous mirrors." In the scene played in front of the bar Wilson effectively cows those within only because the barkeeper and the townsmen, when informed that Wilson is drunk, don't even consider the possibility of merely leaving by the back door as the Mexicans, who are peripheral to the world of Yellow Sky, actually do. It is appropriate also that the drummer, who is closer to the world of parlor cars and marriages than the townsmen, decides to stay within easy access of the back door just in case he should want to emulate the Mexicans' retreat from the conflict that the rest of them accept as in the course of events. In this world the weapon is the gun, rather than manners and mores, because the townsmen as well as Wilson accept it as such. Its efficacy is tacitly agreed upon. In the final scene between Wilson and the marshal, however, new manners and mores come smack against the world of the gun. And it is Potter's final refusal to revert to the old terms of conflict which defeats Wilson. The manners of the "new estate," because the Bride is right there with him, defeat the accepted form of the periodic conflicts. The new alliance of the marshal and the world of the parlor car has won out.

Yet this action has larger reverberations. Potter and Wilson have been described as "ancient antagonist[s]." Potter, who admittedly feels about his marriage as if he has committed his sin in darkness, is nevertheless, as the marshal of Yellow Sky, identified with daylight. Wilson, on the other hand, described as a "midnight cat" while on a tear, turns the town, except for the "street," into darkness. At this moment, while Wilson is drunk and in a rage, the saloon is pervaded by a dark solemnity.

The badman's outbreak, during which for a circumscribed period the traditional roles of authority and order are reversed, suggests that this action in Yellow Sky can be seen as a modern Saturnalia. A sort of Lord of Misrule—as the ruler for such a period was sometimes called—standing for dark and demonic forces customarily kept in tight rein, Wilson assumes authority for the limited period during which he seems virtually omnipotent. Frazer tells us, in *The Golden Bough*, that such reigns occur in an intercalary period "between the old and new." This figure of drunkenness and revelry, opposed to the forces of reason and order, and in parody of the figure of normal authority, is of course doomed to a short reign. He is replaced, as has been expected all along, by the traditional figure of power and authority. His reign, an interlude of indulgence, is to be seen, then,

as a period of release for all the forces which have been effectively controlled during the entire time of constituted rule. But
even though this seizure of dark power for disorder is a not unexpected release, it still poses a definite threat. Quickly becoming unbearable, it must be succeeded by the re-establishment of
the customary restraints of law and morality.

The nature of this rite of conflict and supersedure suggests
an Apollonian-Dionysian opposition. The Apollonian force is
based on the *principium individuationis*: it insists upon morals,
forms, limits, borders, and categories, and imposes the image of
finite humanity upon the disorder of experience. Its counterpart, the Dionysian spirit, recognizes the unity of nature and
experience. Knowing neither limits nor measures, the Dionysian
spirit persists in excess, exuberant expression, and amorality.
Opposed to Apollonian limits and morality, Yellow Sky's outlaw is such a Dionysian figure. During his periods of Misrule,
which he assumes recurrently but which have always been tacitly condoned, the marshal waits for the town to have had
enough of the excess of the fool's rule. He then re-establishes
order.

But the Apollonian-Dionysian opposition seems to move
through the story in other, more subtle ways. The Apollonian
temper is associated with reason and speech, while the Dionysian
is characterized by drunkenness, noise, and music. Of Dionysus,
Nietzsche writes in *The Birth of Tragedy*: "The entire symbolism
of the body is called into play, not the mere symbolism of the
lips, face, and speech, but the whole pantomime of dancing, forcing every member into rhythmic movement." Hence the importance of Crane's description of Wilson: "The little fingers of
each hand play sometimes in a musician's way. Plain from the
low collar of the shirt, the cords of his neck straightened and
sank, straightened and sank, as passion moved him." Rather
than Arion's affective music, which *tamed* the waves and the
sea, Wilson's noise and sound, "chanting Apache scalp-music,"
is the expression of the unruled forces of a primeval force. Furthermore, when the marshal finally encounters Wilson face-to-
face, the former's new power of speech deserting him for the
moment, there is silence: "Potter's mouth seemed to be merely

a grave for his tongue." But earlier, when Wilson is at the peak of his power and effectiveness, his vociferous demand is described as follows—"he yelled, and these cries rang through a semblance of a deserted village, shrilly flying over the roofs in a volume that seemed to have no relation to the ordinary vocal strength of a man. It was as if the surrounding stillness formed the arch of a tomb over him."

Wilson's shrill cries and "wild yowls" set him off against Potter, the man of speech and reason. In "maroon-colored" shirt, "red-topped" boots, and with face "flamed in a rage begot of whiskey," Wilson's appearance suggests a rampant demonism. Armed with "blue-black" revolvers, this "midnight cat" becomes for an hour the last Dionysian reveler in the washed-out wildness of Yellow Sky. Yet Potter too can be seen as an old reveler, one who has been channeled by law and social function for the purpose of feeding back upon the disruptive forces embodied in the outlaw. Potter's new suit is black, and his hands, "constantly performing in a most conscious fashion," are "brick-red." These hands, one on "each knee," are a reminder of the enflaming possibilities within himself that in prior battles with Wilson have enabled him to overcome his opponent. Those possibilities now appear in a simile revealing his new allegiance. Unlike Wilson, who has turned "loose with both hands," Potter "sat with a hand on each knee, like a man waiting in a barber's shop." Once he had ended another of Wilson's outbursts by shooting him in the leg. In this simile, however, it is Potter who waits, Samson-like, to be shorn of his hair and of a kind of power. Later, when the porter has finished brushing his "new clothes," "Potter fumbled out a coin and gave it to the porter, as he had seen others do. It was a heavy and muscle-bound business, as that of a man shoeing his first horse." This simile again reveals the nature of the process going on within Potter's psyche, for parlor cars, porters, and tips are part of the psychological and social domestication of the "new estate."

The second simile, "as that of a man shoeing his first horse," rhetorically and thematically echoing the earlier one, "like a man waiting in a barber's shop," suggests that Potter's domestication is in the service of greater utility; that for Potter, just as for such a horse, traditionally indicative of the body, of energy, of sexuality, rampant forces have been controlled.* The conjunction of these similes, then, suggests the sexual sublimation of bodily force that is necessary for the development of human culture.

It is of particular point, then, that in the Bride's encounter with Wilson she is seen as "a slave to hideous rites gazing at the apparitional snake." At this moment the snake refers, of course, both to Wilson and the "blue-black revolver" he thrusts "venomously forward." But the snake in this tale tempts not the new Bride; Crane does not use his Edenic myth quite that directly. Rather the snake tempts the man, for it recalls his darker, unconscious self. At the first moment of encounter Potter "exhibited an instinct to at once loosen his arm from the woman's grip, and he dropped the bag to the sand." It is of course of great importance, imagistically and thematically, that when Wilson finally lowers the revolver to his side and accepts that "it's all off," we read that the marshal then lifted "his valise." At the end, the gun, which suggests erotic force and natural chaos, is useless to Wilson and unnecessary to Potter. Potter has survived the first challenge to his "new estate." But it is only when the Bride is present that the confrontation between Potter and Wilson is seen as the manifestation of "hideous rites." In fact, it is not at all clear that Potter himself has seen it as such or that he will ever see it as such in the future. It takes the Bride as symbol of control, form, and conscience to give this particular culmination of the entire episode its new meaning as the satanic threat to the *other world* from which Wilson has been disqualified. It takes, then, a kind of double confrontation for the dispersal of Wilson's shadowy threat. He is put in check by Jack Potter the bridegroom and by the force that is embodied in the marriage.

The new order, made manifest and signalized finally by the marshal's marriage, is foreshadowed in other ways. For the

* Consider, moreover, the etymology of the term *marshal*, which the *Oxford English Dictionary* gives as *marho-z* horse, *skalko-z* servant. The aptness of Crane's simile, whether an instance of fortuity or not, is even more striking when it is noted that the earliest meaning in English for *marshal*, a meaning now obsolete, is *one who tends horses*; esp. *a farrier; a shoeing smith.*

town it comes in the presence of the new drummer who controls and orders the townsmen at the bar with his tales and stories. In short, his control comes through his power of speech (the
"Texans . . . did not care to talk" and the "Mexican sheepherders . . . did not talk as a general practice"), just as later the
marshal, helped by the presence of the Bride, will talk Wilson
down. The drummer, then, like "a bard who has come upon a
new field," is a harbinger of the new order. This "new-comer"
into the territory is also identified imagistically with the world
of the parlor car, a strikingly topical image of an Apollonian
world (*parlour* comes, of course, from the French; hence a parlor car is a place for talk and conversation, the signs indicative
of the new order), and consequently with the "new estate" of
the marshal.

Just as the drummer, with his recitation of tales in a kind of
bardic performance, has held the men within the saloon by engaging their interest in what is new and different, so too does
Wilson later keep them within the building, in a parody of order, by resurrecting what is familiar and customary. His control is marked by noise and gunfire (rather than speech), and
it is expressed most dramatically in his control over the movement of the dog acting as a surrogate figure for the men inside.
In fact, when Wilson approaches the saloon, the barkeeper, still
not an effective part of the new "world," "motioned" the drummer "to remain silent." Since talk, out of place at this moment,
has no efficacy, the barkeeper takes, from beneath the bar, "a
Winchester," which does have. Consequently, the dog episode,
besides functioning as the means for the traditional demonstration of the gunman's shooting skills before the final moment of
true confrontation, anticipates, in Wilson's turning the barkeeper's dog into something "like an animal in a pen," the badman's
desire for control over the town, and realizes imagistically the
success of the marshal whose "nice job" it is to contain Wilson.
Wilson's parody of the order and control invested in the marshal becomes, in larger scope, a parody of man's desire to overcome his natural environment.

There are other images indicative of domestication, form and
control. The "Weary Gentleman" saloon, turned by the closing
of "heavy wooden shutters" into a "solemn, chapel-like gloom,"

is a sanctuary from the province of disorder "out there in the street" where "there's a fight just waiting." Potter's own house presents "the same still front" to Wilson "as had the other adobes." Wilson, "howl[ing] a challenge," is faced blankly with a building that "regarded him as might a great stone god." Of course, it is the parlor car that remains at beginning and end as the crucial sign of the new order; but it has its counterpart in the town saloon attacked directly by Wilson. There, in the midst of fear, the drummer is consoled by a quasi-vision. Again in diction and imagery that suggests the interior of the parlor car, Crane apprehends the source of the drummer's reaction: "balm was laid upon his soul at sight of various zinc and copper fittings that bore a resemblance to armor-plate." The marriage itself, the new order manifested in its own ritual, because it is destructive to the old order, at first "weigh[s] upon" Jack Potter "like a leaden slab." Adobes, saloon, bronze, brass, brilliantly polished wood and leaden slab, all suggest the metallic and heavy constructions of order, form, stability, and protection. Stone house, saloon, and parlor car, shelters from the wildness and the violence exhibited by Wilson, stand always for man's portion of permanence through his civilization. As such each of these requires its protector against an uncongenial invader. Consequently, in the context of the parlor car, even the marshal, despite his new status as a bridegroom, must be defended against, for at that moment he is technically and relatively a threat to the manners and mores of the parlor-car estate.

Buildings as the manifestation of human order and as indications of man's organization of his environment are directly related to the marshal's recent marriage, and in specific terms, to the Bride. Thematic identifications occur through carefully worked out clusters of imagery. The Bride's primary thematic function is evident in the hints of rigidity, hardness, formality, and metallic nature that appear in Crane's initial description. A mixture of femininity and hard control,

She wore a dress of blue cashmere, with small reservations of velvet here and there and with steel buttons abounding. She continually twisted her head to regard her puff sleeves, very stiff, straight, and high.

Resemblances in imagery, skilfully transmuted, identify the Bride with the parlor car.

He [Potter] pointed out to her the dazzling fittings of the coach, and in truth her eyes opened wider as she contemplated the sea-green figured velvet, the shining brass, silver, and glass, the wood that gleamed as darkly brilliant as the surface of a pool of oil. At one end a bronze figure sturdily held a support for a separated chamber, and at convenient places on the ceiling were frescoes in olive and silver.

If we miss this connection between the parlor car and the Bride of the "new estate," Crane repeats the connection, even more explicitly, in an effective montage at the crucial point when Potter's conception of the way to handle his new role as husband-marshal wavers in the face of Wilson's temptation. For some moments Potter rises to the bait. Then—

He was stiffening and steadying, but yet somewhere at the back of his mind a vision of the Pullman floated, the sea-green figured velvet, the shining brass, silver, and glass, the wood that gleamed as darkly brilliant as the surface of a pool of oil—all the glory of the marriage, the environment of the new estate.

The memory of metal and velvet, dark brilliance, and "the glory of the marriage" serves to carry Potter through the town's most recent crisis and his own personal ordeal. We are told that at last it is Potter's "enforced reasoning" that vanquishes "Wilson's rage," and the basis of this enforcement is the Bride as constraint and conscience. But this denouement involves the destruction of an old and significant ritual.

The confrontation of the reveler and the marshal—remember that the term *marshal* has within its compass the meaning also of *one who regulates rank and order at a feast or other assembly, one who directs the order of a procession*—is nothing new in Yellow Sky. The first report of Wilson's outburst moves the townspeople to immediate position. It is the most recent performance of an old play.

. . . the information had made such an obvious cleft in every skull in the room that the drummer was obliged to see its importance. All had become instantly solemn. "Say," said he, mystified, "what is this?" His three companions made the introductory gesture of eloquent speech, but the young man at the door forestalled them.

"It means, my friend," he answered, as he came into the saloon, "that for the next two hours this town won't be a health resort."

The barkeeper went to the door and locked and barred it. Reaching out of the window, he pulled in heavy wooden shutters and barred them. Immediately a solemn, chapel-like gloom was upon the place. The drummer was looking from one to another.

Except for the Mexicans, who are outsiders, and the drummer, who has large reservations, the patrons of the "Weary Gentleman" saloon accept the inevitability of the full performance. In conscious anticipation the remaining men cower until they hear the due notes of the familiar exhibition: "Presently they heard from a distance the sound of a shot, followed by three wild yowls. It instantly removed a bond from the men in the darkened saloon." Appropriately Crane sets his ritual in the terms of dramatic performance: "Across the sandy street were some vivid green grass plots, so wonderful in appearance . . . they exactly resembled the grass mats used to represent lawns on the stage." The ritual-like quality of this treatment, expressed also in Crane's references to the barkeeper in terms of his function, "the man of bottles," and Wilson in terms of his, "he of the revolver," is developed further by the bartender's admission: "this here Scratchy Wilson is a wonder with a gun—a perfect wonder—and when he goes on the war trail, we hunt our holes —naturally." This particular description indicates, moreover, that the ritual is strongly atavistic. It provides another telling metaphor, for the world of nature is Wilson's province; according to the barkeeper, "He's [Wilson's] about the last one of the old gang that used to hang out along the river here."

The same basic metaphor appears again in the final scene where Wilson, incredulous at the information that this time his antagonist has no gun, calls the marshal a "whelp," seemingly in one last desperate effort to associate him with Wilson's natural world. Wilson's unconsciously appropriate name-calling is uncommonly rich. Historically, the term *whelp,* used here as a term of derision, suggests beyond the familiar meaning of *puppy* that of *the young of such wild animals as the wolf, bear, lion, and tiger.*

Whelp, then, serves to identify the marshal with the "fear-stricken" dog of the earlier passage:

At sight of the dog, the man paused and raised his revolver humorously. At the sight of the man, the dog sprang up and walked diagonally away, with a sullen head, and growling. The man yelled, and the dog broke into a gallop. As it was about to enter an alley, there was a loud noise, a whistling, and something spat the ground directly before it. The dog screamed, and, wheeling in terror, galloped headlong in a new direction. Again there was a noise, a whistling, and sand was kicked viciously before it. Fear-stricken, the dog turned and flurried like an animal in a pen. The man stood laughing, his weapons at his hips.

The incident of Wilson and the barkeeper's dog has a decidedly sacrificial cast. Wilson as the locus of rebellion implicitly fixes the town's malady in its principles of order; hence his animus toward houses and public buildings. But his most protracted challenge to order comes in his choice of the dog as a scapegoat. Harassed as the embodiment of the town's ills (ills only in the eyes of Wilson, who stands, of course, for quite a different order of things), the dog becomes an outlet for Wilson's violence. But more important, the dog, by being turned finally into a 'penned-up' animal, becomes exactly what Wilson himself has been to the town: the last of the old gang; domesticated, but only half so; with natural wildness still the potent element of his makeup. In short, Wilson not only attributes his own qualities and vices to this scapegoat vessel but ends by turning the animal into his own metaphorical substance. The animal reacts finally to being 'penned-up,' just as, in a different way, Wilson has reacted. Yet Wilson's derisive laughter, directed in part at his normal role within the town's diurnal course, is also self-directed, for it is also aimed ironically at his own impending defeat. Wilson's laughter reminds us further of the behavior of the porter on the California Express who, in an action symbolically like Wilson's, had skilfully "bullied" Potter. Oppressed, the Bride and the marshal—with a "hang-dog glance" —finally leave the train. But just "behind them the porter stood chuckling fatuously." If "historically there was supposed to be something infinitely humorous in their situation," as we were told earlier, so too is there something humorous both in Wilson's badgering the dog and in the prospect of the town's manhood cowed by a single gunman, who when not drunk is the "nicest fellow in town."

Yet, as we have seen, Wilson later equates Potter with the dog. Such identification is accurate insofar as it reflects Potter in the dining car, the sign of a relatively supra-order of being, but it is decidedly inaccurate as a prediction of the final outcome of events. Wilson hopefully tries to identify Potter with the animal scapegoat, but, finally, it is he who moves away like a beaten animal. Kenneth Burke, in *The Philosophy of Literary Form,* talks of the "scapegoat as a 'suppurating' device (that brings the evil 'to a head')." Wilson's action does have this effect; but the evil and the good have not been so clearly demarked as one would normally expect in a scapegoat ritual. Here, the precise point, in the curve of Crane's action, is that the marshal and the town will make a choice as to what will be considered good and evil. This temporary ambivalence of values, then, helps to explain Crane's effective use of the double scapegoat. While Wilson appropriately chooses the more archaic form of animal scapegoat, the marshal tactitly attributing his own vices and temptations to the delegated vessel, designates Wilson as human scapegoat for the entire town and for himself.

But this individual tension is also fundamentally cultural. We have already considered to some degree the nature and direction of Wilson's public aggression. However, we have still to account for the import of Crane's emphasis upon the marshal's feelings of reticence and guilt. In a section entitled "Apollo and Dionysus" from his *Life Against Death,* Norman O. Brown writes: "The path of cumulative sublimation is also the path of cumulative aggression and guilt, aggression being the revolt of the baffled instincts against the desexualized and inadequate world, and guilt being the revolt against the desexualized and inadequate self." This excerpt may account, in conceptual terms, for the nexus of Wilson's aggression against the town, Potter's—and the Bride's—sense of complicity and feelings of "mutual guilt," and the images and symbols of personal and institutional desexualization that designate the sublimation necessary to the growth of culture.

If we see that in psychological terms Wilson is the external, public manifestation of the marshal's unconscious self, and if we recognize that Wilson is, in a sense, the "outlaw" marshal, we see that the marshal's sense of betrayal and shame is directed not only toward the town that he has served in an official capacity and as a particular kind of person, but also toward the outlaw who has periodically served to initiate the ritual that has enabled the marshal to maintain order. Without Wilson there can be no *ritualistic* re-establishment of communal order. Hence the marshal's marriage, along with his abandoning of the gun for the "little silver watch" purchased in San Antonio, is also a betrayal of the "ancient" ways of Yellow Sky. But because Wilson appears to be a smaller, darker, "blue-black" version of the marshal, Jack Potter's shame, guilt, and sense of treachery are also directed toward this earlier, more primitivistic version of himself. In marrying, he has denied once and for all the town's badman his sporadic occupation; he has, in effect, destroyed a former self.*

If it is accepted that the being Potter has fought in the streets stands, in one sense, for a part of himself, it becomes of some importance to indicate that in systematically and periodically controlling this part of himself the marshal has in the past also resorted to violence. The murderous possibilities, given only the difference that Wilson initiates the potentialities, have been equal for the two. But it is Potter, having been intercepted in

---

* It should be indicated further that "The Bride Comes to Yellow Sky" can be approached fruitfully as a monodrama in terms of precise Freudian functions assigned to the three main characters—Potter as ego, the Bride as superego, and Wilson as id; or in Jungian terms, perhaps—the Bride as anima, Wilson as shadow, and Potter as ego. In one sense, the story is a psychic drama in which the different functions of a single human mind are presented in the guises of separate characters. Their interaction, then, portrays the relationships among these functions.

The conception and execution of the drawings illustrating the original publication of "The Bride" in *McClure's Magazine* in 1898 are singularly appropriate for such a reading. The bodily outlines of the marshal and of his bride, especially in their carriage, are remarkably similar, and the clear-cut identification of the marshal and the badman is made in their close resemblance in figure and appearance. Whether these likenesses result from a perceptive reading of the story by its illustrator, Ernest L. Blumenschein, they remain strikingly apt.

his journey to his "safe citadel" from which "he could issue some sort of vocal bulletin," who nevertheless overcomes his adversary's rage by talk and "so much enforced reasoning." Wilson's outbursts create "an obvious cleft in every skull"; but the satisfaction of the ritual closes this break. In a larger cultural sense, it is Wilson's Dionysian excess brought under control by the marshal, the agent of order and the vessel of Apollonian force, which keeps Yellow Sky distinct from the old river-home of the badmen. Just, in fact, as the marshal is associated with the town of Yellow Sky as "his corner," and more specifically with his stone house, so too is Wilson identified with the river, formerly the untamed home of the old gang, and now with the street.

It is probable that, like the town, the marshal stands between two forces of attraction. His temptation in the face of the "hideous rites," hardly casual, involves a decision on his part which will have ramifications for "his town." But the exact nature of these attractions is revealed in still another way in two remarkably related passages.

The first of these excerpts occurs early in the story.

He, the town marshal of Yellow Sky, a man known, liked, and feared in his corner, a prominent person, had gone to San Antonio to meet a girl he believed he loved, and there, after the usual prayers, had actually induced her to marry him, without consulting Yellow Sky for any part of the transaction. He was now bringing his bride before an innocent and unsuspecting community.

Potter's passion has taken the form of love. He has gone to San Antonio and "induced" the girl "he believed he loved" to marry him; his orderly suit has been, "after the usual prayers," successful.

But this suit has its complement. The marshal, in absentia, is himself wooed by Wilson.

The name of Jack Potter, his ancient antagonist, entered his mind, and he concluded that it would be a glad thing if he should go to Potter's house and by bombardment induce him to come out and fight. He moved in the direction of his desire, chanting Apache scalp-music.

When he arrived at it, Potter's house presented the same still front has had the other adobes. Taking up a strategic position, the man howled a challenge. But this house regarded him as might a great stone god. It gave no sign. After a decent wait, the man howled further challenges, mingling with them wonderful epithets.

What Crane has done effectively in the two passages is to offer the basic conflict in either fundamentally similar terms or their opposites. In the second, a suit of passion is again expressed, but rather than "love" it is designated as "desire." Wilson's challenge is really a suit to an empty house, and we have already seen the imagistic identification of house—parlor car—bride. If the prelude to Potter's proposal and "marriage" is composed of the "usual prayers," the aftermath of Wilson's unsuccessful suit becomes the howling of "challenges" and "wonderful epithets." Hence "induce[d]" appears in both passages (and nowhere else). The conjunction of these passages both defines the opposing claims made upon the marshal and reveals the similarity of their basis. The fundamental difference, however, is that Wilson's suit of violence and desire in the streets of Yellow Sky stands as a demonic parody of the marshal's proposal in the parlors of San Antonio.

The personal drama in this case is a further analogue of the larger human conflict of civilization and primitive nature. The intercalary state of Yellow Sky, still in transition between the human chaos which is unruled nature, and man's controlled, ordered, perhaps mechanized, civilization, is rendered imagistically. Crane tells us: "To the left, miles down a long purple slope, was a little ribbon of mist where moved the keening Rio Grande. The train was approaching it at an angle, and the apex was Yellow Sky." The geographical apex that is Yellow Sky is not only dependent upon the two physical and spiritual forces, railroad and river, but appears to be temporarily suspended between them. Of course it is one of the burdens of Crane's story to chart the contest of these opposing forces, which are present in the framework of the town in the specifically acknowledged opposition of the marshal and the remaining member of "the old gang." Consequently, with Wilson explicitly identified with the river and Potter with the railroad, Yellow Sky, at the end moves with the "new" marshal away from Wilson.

The movement from the order of nature toward man's civilization is hinted at throughout. There are only three references to the river, but their effect is cumulative. As the "newly married pair" approaches Yellow Sky, the river is called the "keening Rio Grande." Later, when the narrative turns to the "newcomer" in the saloon, we read that "the fresh-cut bank of the Rio Grande circled near the town." The third reference occurs when Wilson is explicitly associated with the river: "He's about the last one of the old gang that used to hang out along the river here." Like Potter, a "man waiting in a barber's shop," the river has been, in part, domesticated. And the dirgelike sound of the "new" river with its "fresh-cut banks" anticipates the demise of Wilson the "simple child of the earlier plains." If, then, the town, just as the marshal, leans toward the "new estate," it is also clear that the California Express has made grave inroads on the old world of the river. But nature cannot be wholly domesticated, cannot be brought entirely under control, any more than can Potter's darker self ever be wholly exorcised. Even what at first seems like a cursory detail about the railroad, "They have to take water here," observed by Potter "from a constricted throat and in mournful cadence, as one announcing death," suggests that underlying the shifts of power and dominance is a bedrock of permanent forces in elementary opposition. But the old positions and specific conditions of interaction have disappeared permanently. It is no overstatement that the marshal "knew full well that his marriage was an important thing to his town." In fact, "It could only be exceeded by the burning of the new hotel."

COMMENT

"The Bride Comes to Yellow Sky" has been described in various ways: it is an "ironic comedy of fear," a "funny parody of neo-romantic lamentations over 'The Passing of the West,'" the "tale of a childlike man confronting a new, and more complex, situation than his simple code allows for," and—most often—a "Wild West story" crossed with the "anti-climactic Western-humour tradition." Yet although it has been widely anthologized, the story seems never to have been accorded the close structural and textural attention it merits; an attention, in fact, that Crane's other work, notably *The Red Badge of Courage* and "The Open Boat," has received in the last dozen years. The critical method used in the essay, stressing the esthetic and thematic function of reflexive diction, image clusters, the double-self (or "split-image"), and an Apollonian-Dionysian ordering, illuminates some of Crane's other tales, specifically "The Blue Hotel."

The double-self motif is central also to Conrad's *Heart of Darkness* and "The Secret Sharer" and to such other diverse stories as D. H. Lawrence's "The Prussian Officer," Poe's "The Man of the Crowd," and Melville's "Bartleby." The artistic and thematic use of the Apollonian-Dionysian pattern, so central in tragic drama, has not yet been widely investigated by critics of fiction. Its aptness is discernible in Hawthorne's "The Maypole of Merry Mount" and "My Kinsman, Major Molineaux." But the extent to which this approach may be used fruitfully is suggested by its striking applicability to such a seemingly unlikely candidate as Mary Wilkins Freeman's "A New England Nun," a story which owes it fame to the fact that it has been read almost exclusively as an out-and-out example of local-color regionalism.